HELPING YOUR AGING PARENT

A Step-by-Step Guide

REVISED

WILLIAM J. GROTE

Boomer Books
VISTA, CALIFORNIA

Boomer Books
915 Vale View Dr., Vista, CA
www.boomer-books.net
info@boomer-books.net

Illustrations by Matt Kim
Cover design by Cathi Stevenson
Edited by YuAn Chen

ISBN: 978-0-9717373-1-0 (print)
ISBN: 978-0-9717373-2-7 (ebook)

Library of Congress Control Number: 2022917008
© Copyright 2022 by Boomer Books

DISCLAIMER:

Recommendations

Mr. Grote's writing demonstrates a compassionate and intensely personal journey as he travels a very difficult road with his mother as her aging brain begins to sink into dementia. Instead of boring the reader with morose details about aging and dementia, he brings levity and his personal meaning to this often-devastating process. Mr. Grote writes from a personal perspective in almost a conversational tone which should resonate with others looking to keep their mind, emotions and problem-solving abilities above water as they navigate with their own loved ones.

—*Carole Beyers, PhD, Clinical Psychologist*

Just when my father was diagnosed with the onset of Alzheimer's, I read William Grote's book. The story of his journey with his mother's declining health into dementia provides a roadmap highlighting the experiences that are applicable to all adult children like myself. I know that this will be my reference book as I anticipate to start the journey with my father.

—*Caroline Huang, ED. MA, author of* Chinese Parenting Book, *co-author of* 26 Basic Phonograms. *Founder of Mustardseed International Consulting LLC.*

William Grote's latest edition of his book, *Helping Your Aging Parent* is a Must Read for every child with elderly parents. Through his own story, he gives us a solid process for helping our aging parents. Now that I'm reaching that final stage of my own life, I plan to give a copy of *Helping Your Aging Parent* to each of my three kids, now middle-aged adults with their own families. I face a rare, incurable heart disease, so giving them the information and tools to deal with me is an important asset for us, as a loving family.

—*Boku Kodama, Publisher, www.SilentStory.Org*

William Grote's history in journalism is evident in this well-researched g book. His personal experience in managing his mother's declining p health, dementia, need for assisted living, adds humility, empathy, an of levity to the challenges faced by adult children in caring for elde Grote's values in honoring his mother for her unique self, make I'd feel confident recommending to my own adult children (

—*Sheri McGregor, M.A., author of the* Done With The Crying *estranged adult children and founder of RejectedParents.N*

Special Thanks to:

YuAn Chen, for her hard work at editing out the redundancies, misspellings, and grammar mistakes in my writing.

Lorie DeWorken of *MINDtheMARGINS, LLC* who helped to put this book into type and gave it a style.

Lori Hall-McNary, from taking time writing her own *Rockin' L Ranch* mysteries for middle-grade teens to help me. Lori's keen eye and unique ability to cut extra words, like a sidewinder shimming through sand, helped me trim pages of dry drivel.

Laurence Jacobs for taking time from his day job of editing books for Craftsman Book Company to focus his laser vision on this book to locate the last-minute errors we had all overlooked.

Matt Kim, for the illustrations that he was able to draw on demand while sipping coffee at Starbucks.

Sheri McGregor, for her kind encouragement while writing her own book, *and Done with the Crying*. Sheri suggested I revise the original *Helping ...ng Parent* and sprinkle in the adventures I experienced firsthand. She ...d and share the levity that moments of humane caregiving offer.

...*Book Cover Express* whose creative flair helped shape a ...ng peace to the minds of those faced with the chal- ...t.

Table of Contents

There are some outward signs you can easily spot that indicate a serious health problem is forthcoming.

Chapter 1

DOES YOUR AGING PARENT NEED YOUR HELP?

My sister and I were used to a very independent mother. My parents were divorced for over 20 years and my mother never remarried. Mom had a teaching career, retired, painted in oils, did volunteer work, and seemed content living alone. She was part of our lives but had her own interests. We never expected anything for her but a self-reliant life. I'm sure that she felt that way as well.

A few "clues" along the way should have woken us up to her changing needs. Like when she called me soon after signing a contract for an earthquake retrofit for her home's foundation. She agreed to the high-dollar work presented by a door-to-door salesman.

"He was such a nice man." She purred. I drove over to look at the contract she'd signed and immediately called the salesman to give him hell. Thankfully, he canceled it and agreed never to knock on her door again.

"Oh Bill, I can always count on you." Mom's relief that I took charge made me feel good, but still, I wondered. *How had she allowed herself to get so easily duped?*

Six months later, she suddenly needed to place a large fence right in front of her windows.

"I think people are looking in at night." She glanced over to her large living room window.

"But Mom, that's why windows have blinds. Just close them." I said, puzzled. At that point, I was still in denial of her mental acuity. I mentioned the incident to Sis, and we figured that she was becoming isolated and withdrawn, living independently.

"She's probably depressed, sitting there watching TV all day. Maybe she needs to get out with people her own age more," Sis suggested.

I did some research to see what retirement communities offered. Dancing lessons and social outings were prominent features. I showed what I found to Sis. We were sold on the idea. Now we had just to convince Mom. We arranged several weekend field trips to different facilities.

Some places were darn-right creepy, with the residents walking around with blank stares like zombies. Mom wasn't that old yet—was she? Other communities looked like a lot of fun. I'll cover some of the options for senior housing in more detail in Chapter 4.

After many weekends of checking out facilities, we finally arrived at a place a few miles from her house. It featured individual apartments, a large dining area that doubled as a reception hall for weekly concerts, and an on-staff nursing facility should help be needed. A bubbly social director showed us the options and talked about weekly bus excursions to exciting places.

"Next week, we have a wine tasting at La Loma Vineyards," she gushed. Sis and I exchanged glances. "Sounds good!" We nodded in unison.

On the way back to the car, we walked past the large Olympic-sized swimming pool. I noticed Mom's eyebrows rose as she saw a few men in the pool with the sun glistening off their tanned chests. Sis winked at me. *Was she thinking what I was thinking?* We could use this moment in convincing Mom to stay here.

When we returned to Mom's house, it was dark inside. Her shades were drawn tight, and her television blared news from the front room. Seeing this darkness made Sis and I double up our efforts to convince our mother to move, always careful to mention the single men.

"You know, Mom, rather than sitting here by yourself, you could be at the place we visited. Sitting in that pool." After several months of hearing this from both of us, she relented, and we moved her in.

Once we cleared out her house and put it up for sale, we moved her few remaining belongings to her apartment. Then we signed her up for every imaginable social activity. She was going to yoga, exercise, and field trips, but after a few months, she started resisting. Eventually, I had to pay a visit to the social director and convince her to pester Mom and get her out of her apartment.

"Oh, that's typical. Just leave it to me," she chirped.

Mom did develop a few friends, unfortunately mostly women, but that was rewarding for Sis and me to see. Our efforts were paying off a little bit, and that was better than her being stuck alone in her dark home with the TV blaring all day.

Then one day, she fell at the facility, and she didn't know what had happened to her. Sis took her to the doctor for some tests, but they didn't show anything significant, so we let it go. In Chapter 2, we'll get into how to make the most of a doctor visit with your aging parent, so you'll know what questions to ask and avoid letting problems slip by as we did.

Looking back, I realize now that we were still in denial. The next warning came a few months later when I got a call from the beauty parlor at her retirement home.

"You better get over here. Your Mom's acting strange." The concerned stylist whispered in the receiver.

What could be wrong with her? When I arrived, Mom was in the stylist's chair, fumbling with her checkbook over and over.

Very gently, I leaned in. "What's the problem, Mom?" she looked up, and seeing me, it was as if the needle on her record had suddenly sunk back the groove, "I think I'm out of checks." She smiled, a confused look on her face. I paid the stylist and quietly walked Mom back to her apartment, but I was worried.

Later I told my sister what had happened. "Oh, she's probably skipping her blood-pressure pills." Relieved, I told Sis I'd ask the retirement home to administer Mom's pills daily. It cost extra, but Mom needed it. After that, Mom started to imagine that people in the facility didn't like her. She told me that Sis's husband was coming into her apartment when she wasn't there. Our mother needed help. *What now?* We weren't sure what to do or where to go. But we had to do something. Mom was getting worse, not better.

A week later, I received a call from Mom, "Bill, can you come by and take me to lunch? I'd really like a hamburger."

"Didn't Sis already take you?" I asked.

"No, I'm hungry, and she never showed up," she replied.

I immediately called my sister to confirm. Nonetheless, not wanting to disappoint, I showed up to take Mom to lunch again. After two bites of her hamburger, she asked the waitress for a box and asked to go back to the home. When I placed it in the fridge, I noticed the box parade of half-eaten sandwiches filling her refrigerator.

"What's going on here?" I asked gently, pointing to the cartons.

"Those belong to the maids," she replied without skipping a beat. I suddenly felt the room spinning out in my own denial. She looked normal, just like the Mom we knew, but what happened definitely wasn't normal.

I consulted with Sis. We found out that our Mom was eligible for a geriatric screening at a local medical center through Medicare. The examination, which entails a battery of mental and physical tests, took several days and an overnight stay. It took a lot of convincing to get her to try it.

"I don't want to stay overnight somewhere," she complained.

"But Mom, we need to find out what's wrong with you so we can fix it. A lot of guys will be trying to help you." I harkened back to men in the pool.

The geriatric screening was very thorough, compared to the simple battery of tests her doctor had given her. She enjoyed the attention from the different doctors. Still, she was diagnosed with dementia, a deterioration of the mental pathways caused by mini-strokes. We were advised that she could no longer be left alone. We had to scramble to find her new housing with 24-hour care. The sight of her returned to us in a medicated state ended our denial stage. Now, we had new problems to deal with. In Chapter 7 I'll detail some of the ways we dealt with mental issues and dementia. Reading it should save you a lot of pain and grief and maybe even offer you a few laughs as you start down that road. You'll need them.

Preventing Molehills from Becoming Mountains

Major barriers may stand between you and your parent's needs. Overcoming these will require ingenuity and teamwork with your siblings. Everyone needs to be on board with the decisions. Please consider the Family Commitment Pledge Form at the end of this chapter for a semi-formal start. The essentials you and your siblings should consider are:

- Admit there's a problem.
- Overcome your denial and form a united front to help your aging parent.
- Learn to break the invisible shield of authority between parent and child.
- Learn ways to communicate openly with your aging parent. This may require some forgiveness on both sides.

A lot of us tend to ignore the early signs of our parents' decline. I sure did. It's easier to dismiss a forgetful moment as a brain fart rather than face the reality of dementia. Many older people have quirks in their behavior that can cover or hide their dementia until it becomes obvious. The seriousness of their situation may ultimately be brought to light by your parents' neighbors, friends, or even a hairdresser. Take their warnings to heart. Sometimes you don't see these things until you get a call that your mother has fallen and broken her hip. Or you get a call from the police that your parent was found wandering lost on the street.

Many seniors fiercely defend their independence. They often hide their weakness, emotionally withdraw, and get angry when confronted about their physical or mental decline. Sound like anyone you know? Because of this desire to remain independent, your parent may avoid asking for any necessary help until it's too late. Because of this, you can all remain in a comfortable state of denial, like my sister and I. Then something disastrous happens, and you'll have to take charge of a situation that grew into a monster like the 1960's horror film "The Blob," about to take over your world.

Who's in Charge Now?

Whether you realize it or not, there's a force that keeps you from probing into your parent's private life. It's like an invisible shield around them, protecting them from your doubts about their competence. They are, after all, your parents—and usually the most central adult role models you've had in your life. There'll never be a complete reversal of the parent and child roles, but we may need to help manage their life now. Getting through the invisible shield of authority that surrounds your image of them may be a struggle. Don't be afraid to take that step, but remember that you're dealing with your parents—and always show them the respect and dignity they deserve.

Forgiveness—the Beginning of Healing

It's crucial to resolve old issues that you may hold onto—especially if they prevent you from communicating and connecting with your aging parent. You need to move forward, forgive your parent's past wrongs, and ask them to forgive you too. No one's perfect. At this stage in your life, you may have to admit that they did the best they could—even if you feel wronged, neglected, or even abused. If you have kids of your own, you can easily understand that children aren't always easy to raise. Your parent was probably doing their best at the time.

It's funny how we magnify our hurts. They become a disproportionate part of our memories. Sometimes they can take over our lives. Did you know that forgiveness actually induces healing? Numerous studies from all over the world show that people who can forgive are much happier and emotionally well-adjusted than those who can't. According to these clinical lessons, the art of forgiveness can bring about significant psychological and physical changes in the person doing the forgiving. Forgive your parent today. It'll do you all a world of good.

HELPING YOUR AGING PARENT

EXERCISE: How to Forgive

Studies from the Johns Hopkins School of Medicine have shown that the act of forgiveness can reap huge rewards in the health of the forgiver. Forgiving can lower the risk of heart attack, improve your cholesterol levels, and reduce your blood pressure. It also can help you sleep better and reduce levels of anxiety, depression, and stress. But exactly how can you do it?

Forgiveness is not just saying the words, "I forgive you." It's a deliberate process where you decide to let go of negative emotions surrounding the person you forgive, in this case, your aging parent or your sibling. When you let go of your anger toward the person who wronged you, other emotions can eventually filter in. You can start to see the world from their point of view.

According to Karen Swartz, M.D., Director of the Mood Disorders Adult Consultation Clinic at the Johns Hopkins Hospital, there are deliberate steps to take for forgiveness. I've applied them to how they may affect you in dealing with an older parent.

Reflect and remember.
That includes the events themselves when the person wronged you, how you reacted, how you felt, and how the anger and hurt have affected you since.

No one is perfect, even if they think they are.
If your aging parent wasn't an ideal parent, try and see parenting from their point of view. What might they have been going through? What struggles did they face when you were growing up, and they were trying to raise a family? If you have children, can you relate?

Forgive deeply and completely.
Realize that no one is perfect. It allows you to resume a normal relationship with the other person, even if that person never apologizes. What's more important is what's in your heart.

Let go of expectations.
A spoken apology to your parent may not change your relationship with them or elicit an apology in return. However, your apology may help set you free from any grudge you've held against them. Refrain from expectations about your parent's response. Then you won't be disappointed. Forgiving is for your self-healing.

Decide to forgive.
Once you make that choice, seal the deal with action. Forgive your aging parent while they're still alive. If you don't feel that you can talk to them, share your thoughts with your siblings. Your openness may help them heal as well.

Forgive yourself.
The act of forgiving includes forgiving yourself. The way you responded to your parent's wrongs may not have been perfect. Forgive yourself. You probably did your best to cope or weren't mature enough to deal with it. Don't hold past mistakes against yourself now.

At this time, you should start to overcome denial and realize that your aging parent's life is nearing an end. You have an opportunity here to end old grudges and forgive each other so you can heal and move on.

A Small Apology Can Bring Changes

You're starting off on what may be a long and challenging journey together with your aging parent. It's vital to begin on the right path. You can smooth the road ahead by resolving old conflicts and filling in those emotional potholes. One of those small ways to start the healing is to apologize for some past behavior. A small apology costs little and can lead to more extensive talks of forgiveness and offer you a way to break the barriers. Each time you visit your parent in the early stage of your caretaking, ease into conversations about how things were when you were growing up. It makes a great after-dinner or before bedtime conversation and can bring you closer.

This step sets the groundwork for your caregiving. Get to know your parent as a person rather than a parent. Drag out the old photo album and ask them what they were thinking during different times in their life. Use this time to find out what their hopes and ambitions were. What did they start out to do with their life? Find out what or who encouraged them to do what they did. You may find out you have a lot in common. You might even start to appreciate the sacrifices they made in their life. At least you'll develop an understanding of some of the difficulties they faced. Your road to forgiveness always begins with understanding. I used to think that my Mom didn't like me as much as my sister, but a few times she shared something about her past that made me feel she may have been abused and didn't trust men. As time went on, she began to trust me more, but I felt I had to earn it. Your parent's shortcomings may be rooted in the past, and they were really doing their best. I know my Mom must have been.

How to Determine If There's Really a Problem

You probably wouldn't be reading this book unless you noticed a change in your parent's behavior. Sometimes it's something that you can't quite put your finger on. Here are a few things to watch for when you visit them.

General Changes in Habits or Behavior
Changes in your aging parent's habits or attitudes toward you or others are something to watch out for. Has their mood changed? Are they angry for no reason? Or crying without a cause? Is their memory slipping? Are their problem-solving abilities up to par? Are they having problems sleeping? Are they suddenly suspicious of others?

The Car
For many older people, the car is their symbol of independence. How they treat their car can quickly provide you with a barometer of your parent's hidden condition. Are they driving less often? Is it kept cleaned and

washed? Is it in need of repairs? Have the tires gone bald? Is the insurance up-to-date? Check the registration on the license plate. My mother had let her registration lapse for years before she'd quit driving. It's a wonder she never got cited. How your aging parent's car is maintained may hold a lot of answers to the possible condition of your parent.

Forgetfulness

We all become a little more forgetful as we age. Is your parent forgetting things that should be important? Can they tell you where they had their last meal? Have they forgotten where they've put essential items like their phone or wallet? Do they forget important dates? If they take a bus to get where they're going, have they forgotten which bus to take or where to get off? Do they ask you the same question over and over?

Overdue Bills

Keep an eye on the mail. Are bills overdue? Is your parent having difficulty figuring out which they've paid and which they haven't? Are they getting excited by fake checks sent in the mail? There are a lot of scammers looking for easy targets: older people they can take advantage of. Older people living alone seem to attract phone solicitors and door-to-door salesmen. Sometimes they just enjoy an opportunity to talk to someone—the next thing they know, they've bought something they don't need or can't use, like my Mom with the earthquake retrofit.

Changes in Hobbies

Has your parent lost interest in hobbies or social activities that used to be important to them? That's a good indication that something is amiss. If your parent had regular activities such as oil painting, stamp collecting, playing bridge, or singing with a church choir and has suddenly stopped for no apparent reason, something is up. I remember when my Mom suddenly stopped her oil painting class at the senior center. I barely even noticed and might have been better prepared if I had. Don't let that happen to you. A change is taking place that may soon require your action. The change is only a symptom of a larger problem. Pay attention—it may just be the tip of the iceberg that's slowly floating in your direction.

Warnings from Neighbors
Be especially concerned if your aging parent shows extreme responses toward other people, such as anger, anxiety, or paranoia. This could be directed at a total stranger, a neighbor, a friend, a family member, or even you. My Mom thought my brother-in-law had a key to her apartment and was using her refrigerator to store his sandwiches, which was irrational. If your parent appears serious about what you think is an imagined threat, don't just disregard it. They may act on it. Look into it. Listen to what they say and listen to what others say. If a neighbor takes you aside and explains that your parent has been acting strangely and then proceeds to tell you some shocking story you find hard to believe, look into it! Elderly neighbors tend to look out for each other, so there may be some truth in what you're hearing.

Can You Read the Signs?
There are some outward signs that can help you quickly spot symptoms that may indicate a serious health problem is forthcoming. Watch for a sore or a wound that doesn't heal—it could be more serious than you think. Is this sore on their face or arms? It could be skin cancer. Does your parent have incontinence? Do they have problems urinating or eliminating? Urinary tract infections are pretty common in older people. Any type of infection, even in their teeth or gums, strains other body systems. Look at the color of their skin. Do they appear pale? Is there a yellow or orange tint to their skin that would indicate jaundice? How about bruising? Is there a sign that they might have had a fall and are trying to hide it? Are their eyes clear and bright, or are they dull? Do they complain about clouded vision? Does your parent breathe hard after a short walk, or do they have swelling in their legs or ankles? What about tremors of any kind? Do their hands shake?

The Parent Health Evaluation Checklist in *Figure 1-1* is designed to help you evaluate your parent's need for help and possibly your need to step in and take action. Next to any symptom is a box to check off. Take note of how many you've checked off. You may need to take immediate action. If you've noticed any symptoms I've discussed or any on the checklist, take your parent to a doctor for a complete physical exam.

Parent Health Evaluation Checklist

Major Signs of Decline

Your parent had a medical emergency ☐

Someone alerted you to a problem ☐

Mental Changes

Is there a pervasive change of mood? ☐

Have they recently given up a hobby? ☐

Have they become less social? ☐

Are there unopened bills lying around? ☐

Is their house disorderly and dirty? ☐

Is the car dirty or the tires deflated? ☐

Have the car registration and insurance lapsed? ☐

Are they behaving differently toward neighbors, friends or family? ☐

Physical Signs

Are there any obvious signs of a health decline? ☐

Are they short of breath? ☐

Is their skin color normal for them? ☐

Are their legs or ankles swollen? ☐

Do they complain of new aches and pains? ☐

Do they have a new cough? ☐

Do they complain of headaches? ☐

Have they lost their appetite? ☐

Do they seem lethargic or unusually inactive? ☐

_____ **Total boxes checked**

Figure 1-1 *Parent Health Evaluation Checklist*

Make Sure Your Parent Visits a Doctor

Any symptoms listed in the checklist should serve as a wake-up call that your help is needed. If a health problem goes untreated and your parent refuses to address it, you'll have to overcome the shield of authority and get them to a doctor. Preparing for the visit is covered in more detail in Chapter 2. Below are just a few typical health problems that affect older people, some of which are no cause for alarm. However, that's best decided by a physician.

Skin Problems

You may occasionally notice a reddish-brown or purple area on your parent's forearm. It can look as if your parent has been knocked around by a mysterious assailant. These marks are probably just bleeding under the skin caused by a simple bruise. This is common in older people. Their skin is thinner and has less cushioning against impacts. Most of these spots disappear on their own. But if they don't go away in a reasonable time, or bleed, have the doctor check them out.

As the body ages, the skin may become dry and itchy. If your parent has a constant itch and their eyes or skin looks yellowish, have the doctor assess for jaundice or other conditions. Itchiness is a good reason to make an appointment to see the doctor.

Face Pains

Shooting pains down one side of their face may indicate a condition called trigeminal neuralgia. This nerve can go haywire in older people, causing pain and occasional facial twitching. Your parent may fear that they're having a stroke. Tell the doctor. If it's trigeminal neuralgia, there's medication to control it.

Painful Joints

Stiff, painful, or swollen joints in the hips, knees, and spine, especially in the morning, may be caused by osteoarthritis. This is the most common of all joint disorders. Eventually, everyone gets it in some form or other if they live long enough. Usually, an X-ray can determine if osteoarthritis is the cause of joint pain.

While there is no magic cure for osteoarthritis, losing weight and exercising—like daily walks—will help. Yoga may offer some relief and offer a way to socialize as well. You could attend with them as well; it might bring you closer together. There are also several drugs and over-the-counter products that may offer some relief. Acupuncture may also provide some comfort and is covered by many insurance plans. The remedies are much cheaper and less complicated than hip or knee replacement surgery. Sometimes doctors push surgery. Always talk to a specialist about alternative treatments before resorting to the knife. You'll probably have to be your parent's advocate now. Older people heal very slowly and are prone to complications from surgical procedures.

Osteoporosis
This sneaky disease is seldom discovered until after a fall or injury. Then you find that the once-strong bones are now barely holding everything together. Today, a modern procedure called a bone-density scan can immediately alert you if your parent is in danger of osteoporosis. This might be something you'll want to ask the doctor about.

If your parent rates low on the scan results, be proactive and ask the doctor about supplements. They may advise your parent to take calcium and vitamin D to help their body to absorb the calcium. Perhaps they might advise taking boron, a micronutrient for bone growth and maintenance that also helps the healing process. Exercise can also sustain bone mass, especially walking, riding a stationary bike, and lifting weights. Yoga and exercise classes may be offered at your parent's local senior center.

Severe Headache, Numbness, Vision, and Speech Difficulties
Watch for signs of a stroke. A stroke occurs as a result of disturbed blood flow to the brain. We've all heard the term "hardening of the arteries." The arteries are lined with a build-up of plaque that eventually hardens and constricts the blood flow. Little pieces of plaque can break away from the

artery wall, get carried into smaller blood vessels in the brain, become lodged there, and cut off blood flow to that area.

There are different types of strokes. Some are mild, and the effects aren't noticeable right away. Others are stronger and result in temporary numbness, slurred speech, dizziness, or headaches. These are more easily recognized and treated. More severe strokes can lead to temporary or permanent paralysis.

The American Stroke Association has an acronym called FAST to help identify stroke symptoms. FAST stands for:

F: Face Drooping
A: Arm Weakness
S: Speech Blurred
T: Time to call 911

Small strokes, sometimes called transient ischemic attack (TIA), can cause vascular dementia, common among the elderly. It may take several strokes before the signs begin to appear. Larger strokes may only affect a portion of the brain and disable certain parts or functions of the body. The victim may blackout and wake up to find that they cannot speak or move parts of their body. Major strokes can cause massive hemorrhaging and immediate or eventual death. Strokes and coronary artery disease are the largest single cause of death in the U.S. Both conditions are caused by roughened artery walls or plaque build-up over the years. If your family has a history of strokes, you should have their blood cholesterol checked by a doctor. This information should be included in your parent's and all your family's medical records. Have your own cholesterol checked while you're at it.

Fainting Spells

Fainting can be caused by many things, some serious and others not so serious. If fainting results from a spinning sensation, accompanied by a weak feeling in the arms or legs, a tingling feeling, or blurred vision, it could be a stroke. Call 911.

If dizziness occurs when they suddenly stand up from a sitting or lying position, it's usually caused by a temporary drop in their blood pressure.

Fainting or dizzy spells are the most dangerous because they can result in falls, causing more serious injuries, such as broken bones. Broken bones for the elderly usually require surgery and prolonged hospital stays. Often, the underlying cause of dizzy spells can be easily treated. Your parent may need to have their medication adjusted.

Swollen Ankles

Swollen ankles can indicate water retention, early stages of kidney failure, or congestive heart failure. Even though this sounds ominous, even congestive heart failure is not immediately life-threatening if treated. There are drugs that can lessen the symptoms. If your parent has swollen ankles, get them to a doctor as soon as possible, and make sure the doctor provides a remedy for the problem. Don't leave the doctor's office without scheduling a follow-up visit with a specialist to get at the root of the problem. Remember, you are now stepping into the role of becoming your parent's advocate.

Urinary Problems

If your parent seems fatigued and complains of vague pains or burning when they pee, it might be a urinary tract infection. If left untreated, an unassuming urinary tract infection can seem to bring older people to the edge of craziness. Their mental state can really suffer from the loss of electrolytes. Urinary tract infections are easy to cure with sulfa and antibiotics. Usually, one doctor visit can do the trick. But don't let it go untreated.

If you notice the smell of urine around your parent, see a spot on their clothing or bed that indicates they've had an accident, they may be suffering from incontinence. You need to have a private talk with them about their inability to control their bladder. They may not realize that anyone can tell. And it's much better if this little talk comes from you rather than someone else. Remind them that it's really a common problem. In fact, over 30 percent of people over the age of 60 have some degree of incontinence. Fortunately, it's not a life-threatening condition. However, it can lead to a skin rash that can lead to infections as well as embarrassment, loss of dignity, and depression if not taken care of.

Before you break out the adult diapers, ask your doctor to recommend a urologist specializing in geriatric patients. They can prescribe drugs and exercises to help an older patient regain control over their bladder. Some senior care centers even have special clinics designed to help seniors with incontinence. There are Kegel Exercises for men and women you can find online at the Mayo Clinic. There are also specialized Yoga exercises to strengthen the bladder you can find online using the search term "bladder training."

Your parent may have already invested in adult diapers. Ask them what else they've tried. Check into solving the problem before investing in hiding it with *Depends* or other adult diapers. It may be solved by developing and controlling certain muscles. Having some control over the problem is always better than just living with it and diapers—no matter what those ads on TV may say.

When to Step in and Take Charge

Even though you see the signs of decline, sometimes it's difficult to insert yourself into your parent's life. You may feel that you don't have the right to step in and start making decisions for them. Here are a few suggestions.

Start Talking—the Sooner the Better

Talk with your parent. Both of you need to come to terms with the fact that they need your help, if not now, then in the very near future. Keep in mind that they may be reluctant to lay bare their problems to you. It's tough to acknowledge diminishing abilities or independence. You may have to ease into the discussion. If your attempts are headed off at the pass with "Let's talk about this later" or "Things aren't that bad," change your approach. Find an interesting article in the news or online related to what you want to discuss. Or mention a friend's parent and ask your parent their opinion, and if they've thought about needing your help.

If this approach doesn't work, talk about your grandparents. Do you remember what your parent's relationships were like with them? Did they have to take care of their parents in their later years? What happened? Find out if they've given any thoughts to long-term health care. Try to get them thinking and talking about their future. Get the situation out in the open. Ask them if they've considered making a trust, a will, or a health care directive. Be gentle but firm in your efforts to discuss these issues. Don't give up. Tell them you want to take them to the doctor—just for a checkup. Remind them that you love them and are there to help because you're concerned.

Enlisting Your Family Members' Help

Sometimes a parent is more likely to share certain thoughts or ideas with another family member than you. Don't let this hurt your feelings. The more people help, the lighter the load. Better to share this burden. Sometimes feelings of resentment at carrying the full responsibility of a parent's care can split a family apart. Try not to let that happen. It won't help your parent and will erode relationships. Sometimes the circumstances of an aging parent can dredge up old patterns of sibling rivalries and differences of opinion. You don't need that.

In my family, there was only my sister and myself. And it was my sister who asked for my help. I can only imagine how difficult it would be in a large family spread all over the world to get everyone on board the help train. But your parent will need everyone's help and support. If you're the parent's go-to, consider others' circumstances and put some thought into how each family member might best provide support. When it comes to helping a parent, everyone has something they can offer. We're all endowed with a separate set of gifts, and it may be completely different from what another can do. Utilize the whole arsenal by getting every sibling involved.

If your parent has assets, it's usually in everyone's interest to protect those assets by working together. If your parent doesn't have assets, it's in your parent's best interest for you all to work together to provide the best housing, health care, and attention that you can. After all, isn't that what they gave you? We'll cover that in more detail in Chapter 3, but you can start thinking now as to which sibling might be your best helper with these matters.

Pull your family members together and establish a family committee (either in person or by online meetings) to get everyone involved in making decisions regarding your parent's care. A majority vote should do. Don't let one family member try and dominate your decisions or pull you all into a stalemate. *Figure 1-2* is a sample Family Commitment Pledge Form. Have every family member agree and sign it. Then distribute copies. Having everyone's phone number and email address in one place will help. Also, an agreement on how decisions affecting your parent will be made lays the tracks for the help train to roll on and for what may come next.

Family Commitment Pledge Form

NOT ENFORCEABLE BY LAW

We, the undersigned, agree to help in the care of our parent:

_____

We agree to do our best to assist each other and our parent in all situations. We will call upon each other for emotional support, financial help, and physical help, within reason.

We agree to each take part in key decisions involving our parent's care, either by email, telephone or, if possible, in person. If we are not unanimously decided on which course of action to take regarding our parent's help or maintenance care, we will each have a vote in the decision, and the majority will prevail. We agree to abide by and help put into effect the majority decision. If a decision is tied, we will re-vote until a majority is represented. If stalemated, we agree to request outside mediation from a qualified source.

Name _____ Phone _____ Email _____

Name _____ Phone _____ Email _____

Name _____ Phone _____ Email _____

Figure 1-2 *Family Enlistment Form*

This agreement is a good reminder to have if one of your family members thinks they're too busy when it comes time to help out with your parent, be it a new job, a promotion, or a new baby. Everyone can find excuses when they don't want to do something, but helping your aging parent is something they should want to do. Use this opportunity to create a better relationship with your family, as well as your parent. Work out a way so you can all participate without putting undue pressure on anyone. There's always a way. Working together will strengthen your family bond and bring you all closer. Isn't that what life is all about? Enlist your family's help today! Someday they may thank you for it. Even if they don't, they'll always respect your effort in trying to pull them together.

Early on, denial is often a keyword. You, your family, and your parent can all deny there's anything wrong. If you all ignore the warning signals, don't worry. They'll be plenty more signals to come. But start to act as soon as possible—before the fire engines and ambulances shock you into reality. Get your family together and have that heart-to-heart talk. Give them the current "State of the Health" speech on your parent. Tell them what you've noticed about your parent's behavior. Then get everyone thinking about the future. Ask them if they know whether your parent has:

1. **An Up-to-date Will**—that explains the allocation of their property and assets upon their death.

2. **An Up-to-date Trust**—the legal vehicle that protects their assets from probate.

3. **A Life Directive**—that explains how they want to be kept alive in their last days.

4. **A Death Directive**—that explains how they want their funeral to be.

5. **Preparation for Future Housing**—have they made a down payment for a retirement village?

6. **Long-term Health Insurance**—to pay for their care when Medicare runs out.

7. **Insurance** to pay for funeral expenses.

Each of your siblings should know about the presence (or lack of) of these documents, so you're all on equal footing. You may need to ask your parent about them so you can ensure their wishes and help prepare for their future. We'll get into trusts, wills, and directives in Chapter 3.

Right now, you need to get the communications lines open and flowing in all directions. If you get stuck at this stage and can't seem to move because your parent won't admit they need your help, or you're at odds with an uncooperative family member, you're probably in the majority.

Problems with Siblings

You'll likely have one family member who may give you grief. First and foremost, forgive that sibling in your heart and soul. Picture them in your mind and say to yourself that you forgive them. Let go of any hatred or ill feelings that you've harbored against them, at least for now. Your parent needs you. Picture them again in your mind and tell yourself that you really want them to help. If you are religious, ask for God's help to give you a hand. It never hurts to ask, and you may be surprised to find it works, maybe not in the way you expect, but sometimes in a way you don't expect.

If they confront you and ask what makes you qualified to bring the family together, tell them that someone has to do it. Remind them of the work it takes (and will take going forward) to care for an aging parent. Let them know that you'll need their help to work with you.

Mention the problem to your other siblings. You're all in this together; perhaps someone else has a positive idea. But don't try and alienate anyone, which will only serve to drive you all further apart when you really need to be coming together. Compliment each of your siblings on their strengths and how those powers may be valuable in helping your aging parent. You need everyone's help at this point.

If you become mired in sibling hassles and get to a stalemate, you can turn to outside mediation. You could ask a fair-minded pastor from your church to step in and mediate for you. If this doesn't work, you could hire a professional mediator, but keep in mind that they charge from $100 to $400 an hour or more, so make sure that your family agrees with this before forging ahead.

Mediators can be found at the Academy of Family Mediators, The National Academy of Distinguished Neutrals, and the National Care Planning Council.

Many mediators will offer a free in-person or phone consultation to explain their services. Questions to ask a potential mediator include:

1.   How many mediations have they attended?

2.   Do they have training directly related to elder mediation?

3.   How often do they facilitate mediations?

4.   Are they certified?

Once you get your family onboard the help train, remind them that soon you'll take your aging parent to the doctor. Tell them that you'll report back to all of them on what you've found out.

Use the space on the next page to write down the names, emails, addresses, and phone numbers of all your parent's health care professionals for the next step—the doctor visit.

Parent's Doctor List

Please list: Doctor/specialty/email address/address/phone number

_____

_____

_____

_____

_____

_____

_____

_____

_____

_____

_____

_____

_____

_____

_____

_____

_____

_____

Figure 1-3 *Parent's Doctor List*

Sometimes a doctor will say your parent is "fine"
when your parent is acting downright crazy
and you know for a fact they aren't "fine."

Chapter 2

THE DOCTOR VISIT

I first noticed my mother had a health problem when she began huffing and puffing after we had gone only about 50 feet of her daily walk. I was really shocked. We had to turn back—and this just wasn't normal. Mom played basketball in college and always kept very fit. She included long walks in her daily exercise regimen and continued walking and exercising long after retiring.

"Are you okay?" I asked, incredulously. "You sure you want to head back?" She looked at me defiantly with her hands on her hips, and hissed. "I'm not a young chicken anymore."

She wouldn't admit what I knew: something was wrong. She probably figured her decreasing stamina was part of the aging process.

But it wasn't. After many tests and several doctors, I learned that she had developed congestive heart failure. I wish now that I had noticed her condition sooner. I might have been able to prolong her life—or at least improved the quality of it. And for sure, my sister and I would have spent more time with her had we known.

If you've noticed any health changes mentioned in the previous chapter, you need to investigate as soon as possible. I'm not suggesting you become so vigilant that you check your parent's blood pressure every day or try and act like a doctor. Still, it's essential to act quickly on problems when they become apparent—especially chronic problems that may sneak up on you. Make sure your parent sees a doctor. If you don't, their health will only get worse.

If your parent is reluctant to visit the doctor in person, consider telehealth options. They're reasonably easy to set up as an app on your phone or tablet with your parent's doctor's office or health care provider. This way, your parent can converse with their doctor from the comfort of their own home. In the event of a contagious disease, such as the flu or the COVID-19 pandemic, telehealth offers a safe way of communicating concerns with the doctor before the actual office visit, and may even make the office visit unnecessary. If the doctor sees something concerning, they can diagnose it right over the phone and order meds shipped from the pharmacy. Or they may make an actual in-office appointment as a follow-up. Even in a pandemic, most doctor's offices are safe places as long as you observe health protocols like masking with N95 masks and frequent hand washing.

My sister was the one who first took our mother to a doctor. Sis continued to act on her own until she enlisted my help. I had demands on my time—my young son for one. And if I took off during the days, I would have to work late at the office to make up for my time away. But there were demands on my sister's time also. So, we started splitting up the doctor visits, and it worked out well for both of us. Each trip to the doctor became our own one-on-one special time with Mom. Alone with her, we'd recount old stories or exchange views of what we thought of the doctor or the staff.

Looking back, I'm happy I took those afternoons to be with Mom. If I hadn't, I'd regret that now. Regular doctor visits were vital in tracking her continuing health problems—and she wouldn't have gone without us. Those doctor visits were also meaningful opportunities to become closer and more involved with our mom's life. It also provided us with more clues to offer the doctor.

At first, my mother's doctor visits didn't seem to be getting us anywhere. Mom had been going to the same doctor for several years. He just renewed her prescriptions and gave her a clean bill of health. When my sister and I started going along with her, the doctor seemed reluctant to tell us exactly what was happening to Mom. He also didn't have any answers to our questions. Although we managed to get a prescription to reduce the swelling in Mom's leg, the doctor gave us no explanation of what caused the edema, why she was short of breath, or why her memory was failing.

Mom liked her old doctor. She had known him for years and felt comfortable with his professionalism. Sis and I needed answers, and we weren't getting them. We decided it was time to get a second opinion.

 ## Reluctant to Change?

- Show respect for your parent's trusted doctor.
- Suggest that a second opinion is needed.
- Explain the problem that hasn't been solved.
- Assure your parent that you'll do the research and set up an appointment for a second opinion.

We ended up going to six different doctors, starting with my sister's doctor, who she thought highly of. Most of these doctors were very personable, but they failed to identify the root cause of Mom's symptoms or offer us any real help. Physicians who aren't specialists in geriatric care may not be the best choice for your aging parent. As adult children, you have to be your parent's advocate if you want them to receive good health care. The information that follows should help.

Evaluating Your Parent's Current Health Care

Before making that first doctor visit with your parent, take time to sit and talk with them about their health and the care they've received from their current doctor. Find out when their symptoms developed, their concerns, and what less-obvious problems they've been experiencing that may or may not be related. Find out which doctors they've already been to and what the diagnosis was. Get each doctor's phone number and email. Refer back to your Parent's Doctors List in Chapter 1. Write everything down.

Go to your parent's medicine cabinet and make a list of all the medications your parent is taking, including the strength of the medication and prescribed dosage. Don't leave anything out—even aspirin. Write them down with the dosages and frequencies in the checklist below.

Prescription Drug List

Drug name: _____

Amount prescribed: _____ Frequency _____ for how long? _____

Drug name: _____

Amount prescribed: _____ Frequency _____ for how long? _____

Drug name: _____

Amount prescribed: _____ Frequency _____ for how long? _____

Drug name: _____

Amount prescribed: _____ Frequency _____ for how long? _____

Drug name: _____

Amount prescribed: _____ Frequency _____ for how long? _____

Drug name: _____

Amount prescribed: _____ Frequency _____ for how long? _____

Drug name: _____

Amount prescribed: _____ Frequency _____ for how long? _____

Drug name: _____

Amount prescribed: _____ Frequency _____ for how long? _____

Figure 2-1 *Prescription Drug List*

Educate yourself about each drug, its uses, and side effects by looking them up on the Internet or in a *Physician's Desk Reference* available at your local library. Take a good look at the side effects and see if any reactions sound familiar to what your parent may be experiencing. It's not unusual for elderly patients to have side effects and attribute them to the aging process. WebMD (WebMD.com) has a great drug interaction checker where you can enter the names of prescription drugs, over-the-counter medications, or herbal supplements and find the possible adverse reactions.

Then, go to their kitchen and check for vitamins, health foods, and natural remedies or supplements your parent may be taking. Some people take all kinds of over-the-counter health medications. Your parent may be one of them. If your parent takes too much of a drug or takes it in combination with other medications, or certain over-the-counter remedies, they may have problems. Even natural substances can have side effects. Most people don't bother to tell their doctor they're taking Ginkgo Biloba, large doses of vitamin B, C, or D, or other over-the-counter preparations. The doctor needs to know about any vitamins and natural herbs. Write all these down on the spaces below, and check them out on the Internet.

_____

_____

_____

All sorts of mistakes can occur with medications—especially if your parent forgets whether they took them or not. Double-dosing or taking a dosage that's no longer correct for them are the most common mistakes. If your parent is taking daily medications, as more than half the people over age 65 are, make sure they actually take them daily and in the proper dosage.

According to a study by AARP, 87% of people over 65 years take a prescription drug regularly. On average, they take four different pills every day. Many of these drugs are for high blood pressure, diabetes, heart trouble, kidney problems, or other ailments. You name it, and there's a pill for the condition (or one in development for it). But if they forget to take that pill or take it twice or in the wrong combination, all sorts of side effects can occur. They may become dizzy, nauseous, or even faint for no apparent reason. The cause of an incident can be a mystery. But the results can be devastating.

One morning my sister and I received an emergency call from the urgent care in Mom's retirement home. Mom had passed out and hit something on the way down and cut herself. The cleaning lady had found her unconscious and bleeding in her room. She was rushed to the on-site urgent care, kept for observation, and released several days later. My sister and I never really knew what happened, but we suspected that she might have taken a double dose of her blood pressure pills. After this, we arranged to have a staff member administer her medications every morning. That seemed to work; at least she never passed out again.

Keep Your Perspective

If you haven't seen your parent in some time, keep in mind that the stress of everyday life can make dealing with simple things more challenging as your parent ages. There are bound to be signs of mental and physical decline that are normal and unrelated to drug interaction or pathological problems. Don't become alarmed and rush to classify any medical problem right off the bat. Nothing is worse than an amateur diagnosis.

The minor glitches in your parent's memory don't necessarily mean they have Alzheimer's or some form of dementia. According to the Alzheimer's Association, only 11% of people 65 or older have Alzheimer's dementia. According to the US Library of Medicine, a 70-year-old male has an estimated 26.9% probability of developing dementia. The average 70-year-old female has an estimated 34.7% probability. Your parent may be in perfectly normal health for their age. They may have a minor health problem that has become chronic due to lack of attention. Or they may need a change in a prescription for a drug they've been taking for the last 20 years. They may be lacking some vitamin or mineral or suffering from a slight infection. But you won't know for sure if it's something minor or a major problem without a proper evaluation by a doctor.

The important thing is that your parent may need *your* help now to take care of these problems and make sure they get follow-up health care.

In today's busy health care settings, patients need an advocate to fight for them. This may be especially true for older people. Ageism exists, even in medical care.

To prepare, consider what answers you'll need when you see the doctor:

- What exactly is wrong with your parent?
- What is causing the problem?
- What can you all do to make the problem go away?
- Is there an outlook for a full recovery?
- If there's no outlook for recovery, how can you help your parent cope with what they have?

The key to getting answers is being persistent, organized, and asking the right questions. That means being specific and on task but insistent if necessary.

What Happens if Your Parent Believes Their Old Faithful Doctor?

Some parents have trusted their family doctor for years and may not want to accept the idea of a specialist or another doctor. Here are a few ideas to help them overcome resistance.

- **Listen to their objections calmly.** Not many people enjoy going to a doctor. Try and see it from their perspective.

- **Get a sibling to join you in your struggle.** Sometimes two can be more convincing than one.

- **Set up and connect directly with a doctor online.** While telehealth appointments have limitations, it brings the doctor right to you and your parent. A good doctor can pick up clues from your parent's skin tones and speech patterns to help in an assessment.

- **Offer a reward.** Promise to spend some time with your parent afterward and make it a fun outing.

Include Your Family Members

Before you actually make an appointment with a doctor, get on the phone and call your family members. Tell them what you've seen and why you're concerned. Enlist their support. Utilize the Family Commitment Pledge from Chapter 1. If you haven't discussed this agreement with your family members and had them sign it, now is the time. You'll need it in the days ahead.

Plan on attending the doctor's appointment with your parent. Don't let them go alone. This time is crucial for your family. Keep them informed of what you're doing and, if possible, enlist one or more of them to come with you to the doctor's office. If you don't attend, your parent may not know what questions to ask the doctor. They may not remember what information the doctor gives them. It's better to bring a sibling with you, even if you fill up the examination room. Your presence conveys "This person's health is important" to the doctor, which usually equals better care.

You'll want your parent to have a complete physical. Be there when your parent calls for the appointment, or make the call yourself, so the appointment can include a conference with the doctor for you, your parent, and your family members. Having at least one of your family members along will help you spread the word to other family members. That way, you won't be the lone crusader in your parent's cause. It'll also ensure that you both hear the same thing from the doctor, so there won't be confusion later about what was actually said. If just you and your parent are there, I can almost guarantee, from my experience, you both won't hear the same thing. Some patients focus on the negative, and some on the positive—they rarely have the detachment to get the whole perspective. That's why it's good to have someone along when receiving a diagnosis from the doctor. An objective bystander can ask questions to clarify the results.

Getting Background Information for the Doctor Visit

Bring a current list of your parent's medications for this doctor visit, like the Prescription Drug List at the beginning of this chapter. You might also want to bring your notes on the information you found on the various medications. This will help you discuss your parent's need for the different medications. What are they for? What do they do? What are the possible side effects or drug interactions? You'll have some information, and the doctor can fill you in on the rest. If any known side effects match your parent's symptoms, be ready to discuss them. Write everything down and bring it with you to the doctor's office.

By studying the medications your parent is taking, you'll probably uncover a few things about their health that you weren't aware of. You may be able to piece together a better medical history than your parent can tell you. You may even uncover some problems or complications that have been aggravated by the drugs they've been taking. My Mom was still taking a high blood pressure medication prescribed in the 1970s even though it was later found to cause serious side effects in older people. It's also possible that your parent was prescribed something they don't take. I found that Mom had been prescribed a diuretic, probably to relieve her swollen legs, but never used it.

The swelling in her legs may have been a symptom of a more severe problem that was never diagnosed, such as failing kidneys or the inability of her heart to pump blood properly. You can learn all kinds of information from the prescriptions your parent is taking. Write down your questions so you can quiz the doctor at the physical.

The American Geriatrics Society uses an acronym called **PIMS** for Potentially Inappropriate Medications. Check if your parent is taking any of these medications and bring it up when you visit the doctor. A simple online search can provide you with some knowledge of what may be on the list.

 Websites for Checking Medications

American Geriatrics Society (americangeriatrics.org)
American Geriatrics Society's GeriatricsCareOnline.org
    (geriatricscareonline.org)
Health In Aging (healthinaging.org)

Most doctors have their own opinion on particular drugs. The doctor may pooh-pooh the bad press on this or that drug, or they may take the time to explain to you why some doctors believe a drug is dangerous while others continue to prescribe it. If your parent is taking one of these drugs, ask the doctor if there's an alternative available that might work just as well and offer less risk.

Organize Your Questions

Write down all of the reasons you're there to see the doctor. Fill out the Symptoms Observed and Questions for the Doctor form (*Figure 2-2*) and make a list of concerns. Be thorough. Arriving prepared saves time. Have your questions ready, and take an advocacy role when needed. Your parent may not want to participate in this discussion, but include them when possible. The future of your parent's health could be in your hands.

Symptoms Observed and Questions for the Doctor

Doctor _____ Appointment Date _____

Symptoms noticed:

_____

_____

_____

Questions for the doctor:

_____

_____

_____

_____

Figure 2-2 *Symptoms Observed and Questions for the Doctor*

In addition to pertinent questions, write down a family history of illnesses and causes of death for each of your parent's immediate family. Get your parent to help you. This list will prove helpful for you and your children as well. Many health problems are passed down through genetics. The Family Medical History form (*Figure 2-3*) will help you organize this information.

Use the Checklist of Things to Bring to a New Doctor Visit (*Figure 2-4*) to help you organize all the items and information you need to take with you when you go to see the doctor.

The Doctor

Be prepared for the doctor to clarify your relationship with your parent. HIPAA Privacy Rules have established national standards to protect individuals' medical records and other personal health information. Make this first visit with your parent's current doctor. This doctor is familiar with their problems and just as important, your parent is familiar with them. The familiarity can make the physical examination process a friendlier, less terrifying experience for your parent. You can always take your parent to your doctor or another doctor who specializes in gerontology for a second opinion if you feel it's necessary.

If your parent makes the appointment, call the doctor yourself, explain your concerns and advise them that you'll want to discuss your parent's condition and care. The doctor may have some issues with you intervening on your parent's behalf because of HIPAA Privacy Rules. They'll want to clarify your relationship. Remind them that you're only trying to provide them with information that could help with a diagnosis. They may ask if you have Medical Power of Attorney. Don't worry, in the next chapter, we'll get into advanced options like Power of Attorney, where your parent will assign someone to legally take charge of their medical care. Right now, you're just making a doctor's appointment.

If your parent is enrolled with Medicare, which everyone over 65 is automatically enrolled, make sure the doctor accepts an assignment from Medicare. This means the doctor won't charge your parent fees over what Medicare will pay. In other words, you want to make sure, ahead of time, that the exam will be entirely covered by Medicare. Some older people carry a supplemental insurance policy that will pay the difference between what Medicare pays and what the doctor charges.

Family Medical History

Patient's name _____

Social Security Number _____

Mother's illnesses or cause of death _____

Other pertinent or physical/mental health data _____

_____

_____

Name of patient's father _____

Father's illnesses or cause of death _____

Other pertinent or physical/mental health data _____

_____

_____

Brother's/Sister's name _____

Brother's/Sister's illnesses or cause of death _____

Other pertinent or physical/mental health data _____

_____

_____

Grandmother (mother's/father's side) _____

Cause of death of grandmother _____

Other illnesses or physical/mental health symptoms _____

Grandfather (mother's/father's side) _____

Cause of death of grandfather _____

Other pertinent or physical/mental health data _____

_____

_____

Figure 2-3 *Family Medical History*

Checklist of Things to Bring to a New Doctor Visit

- Health Insurance records
- Medicare Card
- History of past illnesses and operations
- Symptoms and questions form
- Prescription Drug List form
- List of over-the-counter drugs, herbal medications, and vitamins used
- Allergies
- Family medical history
- X-rays or test results (if necessary)

Figure 2-4 *Checklist of Things to Bring to a Doctor Visit*

Most seniors depend on Medicare to cover their doctor's fees. Not every doctor will take an assignment from Medicare. However, I do know of cases where a doctor agreed to take a patient they've been seeing for many years when the patient became eligible. If your parent is covered by an HMO, call the office to determine if the doctor takes patients under that participating provider plan before you make any appointments. You don't want any rude surprises when billed.

If the doctor is willing, discuss your concerns, or email your Symptoms Observed and Questions for the Doctor form (*Figure 2-2*) before the appointment. If the doctor has the information ahead of your visit, it won't look like you're betraying your parent's confidences at the actual exam. That way, the doctor can ask your parent questions based on your concerns. Your parent will be less likely to go on the defensive if the doctor is the one bringing up the issues. Remember, you don't want to alienate your parent. You're now their health advocate—though they may not realize it yet.

Let your parent take the lead during the appointment, especially if the doctor already received your form. Try to resist the impulse to jump in and answer every question, as the doctor may be checking your parent's responses.

If you've mentioned that your parent has been forgetful, the doctor may perform a field test memory exam in which he'll ask tough questions like "Who's the current president?" and "What year is it?"

He may make up a story about Elvis riding a pink Cadillac through Memphis. Then, a few minutes later, he'll ask your parent to recount the story. He may ask for parts of it, like what kind of car was driven, what color the car was, or who was driving it.

You may be aghast, as I was, as your parent struggles to remember the details. Or as they smile and pretend it doesn't matter as long as they can make the doctor laugh.

Be careful, sometimes your parent can finesse the doctor. Don't let the doctor lose their impartiality. If the doctor determines your parent needs a psychiatric evaluation for memory or other cognitive issues, they can recommend one. It usually requires a short overnight stay at a geriatric assessment center in your community. We'll cover the details of this type of examination in Chapter 7. But before you head off for a geriatric evaluation, make sure you have all the legal documents you'll need before you go. We'll go over these in Chapter 3. If you don't have these documents signed ahead of time, it can really complicate matters if your parent is determined not competent.

Follow Up with the Doctor after the Exam

Follow up regarding any tests or blood work within a week. Doctors are busy people and have lots of patients. The doctor will probably be willing to talk with you by phone before scheduling a second exam. They may even ask you questions based on the results of the tests or whether you've noticed any changes in your parent's behavior or condition since the exam.

By calling, or e-mailing the doctor and not waiting for them to contact you, you're showing that you want your parent's health issues resolved promptly. Show the doctor that you care and are willing to explore anything that may help manage your parent's health care. Let the doctor know that you feel there's a problem to address and that you're not going to go away until you get appropriate action from them. This may also help you feel that you're doing all you can for your parent at this stage, which will help you sleep better at night.

Second Opinions

After you have a follow-up talk with the doctor, you'll have an idea about how to proceed. The doctor may tell you that your parent is fine and you can stop worrying. There may be a simple explanation and a remedy for your parent's problem. However, sometimes a cure isn't that simple. Or maybe there's a cure, but the doctor feels it involves procedures that are risky or more than your parent can take. Or your doctor may tell you that your parent is fine when you know better.

If the doctor doesn't recognize the problem or says it's insignificant, get a second opinion right away. As I mentioned earlier, my sister and I consulted six doctors before we finally received a valid diagnosis for my mother's heart failure and dementia. Possibly, the doctors were trying to let us down gently. Mom wouldn't get any better. Knowing this sooner would have led us to manage it quicker, though.

I'm glad we persisted and acquired additional opinions. Eventually, we sought the help of a geriatric specialist (a doctor who specializes in treating the elderly). Look online for a medical referral agency in your area.

 Medical Referral Agencies

Healthgrades (healthgrades.com)
Vitals (vitals.com)
WebMD (webmd.com)

These specialists have received specialized training in treating and managing the problems of older people. Again, be sure to take care of legal issues mentioned in Chapter 3 before sending your parent off on an in-depth medical exam that could determine them to be incompetent.

Accepting the Results

The results from the doctor's exam aren't always pleasant. But knowing the truth can help you plan for the future and figure out what action comes next. The truth can help you overcome the demons of denial and inertia. In the beginning, the doctor will usually make simple recommendations, such as changing your parent's prescription, recommending supplements, and taking further tests. However, the doctor may find things that require immediate care, such as a required surgery, a referral to a specialist, or further tests.

Programs Available to Help Seniors

Don't think that you're totally on your own when it comes to caring for your parent. There's a lot of help out there for seniors. If your parent can still live on their own but can't be bothered to put together a nutritious, balanced meal, order their meals to be delivered by Meals-On-Wheels (www.mealsonwheelsamerica.org). Then you can be sure that they have a hot, healthy meal delivered every day.

If the doctor says your parent needs exercise or social interaction and should get out of the house more often than you can manage, there are some senior programs designed for just that purpose. You can usually find them on the website of your local senior center. Many of these services are staffed by volunteers who may come and pick up seniors who don't have transportation. Social and recreational activities exist to help seniors stay mentally and physically fit. Exercise programs, physical therapy, counseling programs, and group activities to help seniors cope are often fun. Some of these are part of community services. Some are services covered by Medicare or state aid. Some require a small contribution, and some have to be recommended by a doctor. There's a whole world of help out there, and you can start by looking up your local senior center. If you're in a rural area, services may be further away or less available. Check with local churches and charities. If your parent needs customized or ongoing home care, ask the doctor for resources available in your area. Often, they have lists of social services.

Your senior center typically has the inside scoop on activities and help. Here are a few websites that may help also:

- Elder Helpers (www.elderhelpers.org)
- Aging Life Care Association (www.aginglifecare.org)
- National Institute on Aging (www.nia.nih.gov/)

Here are some programs that may be available in your community for helping your aging parent and found with a simple search in your computer browser.

- **Adult Day Health Care**: This is an excellent service for people who are fit enough to attend. You'll need to ask the specific facility for their criteria. They offer a wide range of therapeutic, rehabilitative, and support activities, including nursing, assistance with life activities, social work services, meals, and sometimes even transportation. This service is available several hours a day, usually during weekdays.

- **Elderly Companionship Services**; Companions are available to visit isolated or home-bound individuals for conversation, reading, letter writing, and light errands. Sometimes volunteers from a church or the community at large provide these services.

- **Escort Services/ Homemaker Services for the Elderly**: These services provide personal assistance with shopping, doctor's visits, outings, laundry, light cleaning, dressing, preparation of meals, and escorting your parent to the doctor. You can obtain homemaker help through in-home health care agencies, the Area Agency on Aging, the Department of Social Services, and religious groups and organizations.

- **Home Delivered Meals for Seniors**: Nutritional programs, such as Meals-on-Wheels, offer home-delivered meals to seniors. Subsidized programs ask for voluntary contributions, while others may require full payment to deliver a hot, well-balanced meal.

- **Home Health Aides**: These aides provide home health service and assistance with eating, dressing, hygiene, bathing, administering medications, and light household tasks. If a doctor orders this service, the costs may be covered by state health aid or Medicare (be sure and ask ahead of time).

- **Home Health Care**: There are organized programs that include social work, occupational therapy, physical therapy, and other rehab services to individuals in their homes.

- **Housekeeping Services**: These are volunteer, or fee-based groups, that help with cleaning, shopping, laundry, and meal preparation. Usually, they charge a small fee unless they're volunteers from a church.

- **Housing Assistance**: These volunteer programs help seniors find housing, such as shared housing or emergency shelters. The cost of the housing, or a portion, is usually paid by local government sources.

- **Physical or Occupational Therapy**: These are programs initiated by your doctor to build up the skills your parent needs for daily living. They may be paid in part by Medicare, depending on the circumstances.

- **Speech Therapy**: Help for difficulty speaking, communicating, or swallowing due to stroke or other illness. If the doctor recommends a speech therapist, Medicare usually covers the cost.

- **Social Day Care**: This is like adult daycare, but the activities emphasize group socializing. Usually, transportation is provided.

- **Telephone Reassurance**: This volunteer organization offers telephone contact and socialization to older people who are home alone. They may call every day or a couple of days a week just to make contact and provide assurance.

- **Transportation Services**: Many transportation services, such as Dial-a-Ride, Red Cross Wheels, Cancer Society, and Lifeline, are available for a small fee.

The key here is that once you notice a problem with your parent, you may have to be the one to take action. Older people can become complacent and resist change or anything that takes them into areas of health care. With complacency comes the danger of decline, which can be swift and ruthless with older people.

If you are out of options, a geriatric care manager, usually a licensed nurse or social worker who specializes in geriatrics, can help you and your family to identify needs and find ways to meet them within your community. These trained professionals can help find resources and work with you to form a plan and find the services you need. Geriatric care managers can be especially helpful when family members live far apart from each other and your aging parent. Be prepared to pay out-of-pocket for their services, which aren't cheap. It may cost from $500–$1000 for an initial assessment of your parent's needs, as of this writing. Many of them charge around $100–$200 per hour for their services. You can find them in the Eldercare locator (www.eldercare.acl.gov) or Aging Life Care Association (www.aginglifecare.org), or you can just Google the term "geriatric advisor" into your browser and hundreds of ads will appear. The National Institute on Aging and AARP also have articles that may also appear on your browser. These articles can provide more information on Geriatric

Care Managers and help you decide if their services are a good fit for your family needs.

If you encounter resistance in providing care to your parent, remind yourself that you're doing this to help them and not yourself. Try peer pressure if you can't convince your parent that a doctor's appointment is needed. Have one of their friends or a relative show up to back your cause. Hopefully, your parent will give in and realize they need to let you take them to the doctor.

If you're spiritually-minded, don't forget about prayer; turning to a higher source. I realize this may sound simplistic, but it worked for me. It may work when you're totally out of options with a loved one. Sometimes it's the only thing that does.

*When life and death decisions are necessary, you'll wear
that Power of Attorney for Healthcare like a badge and
hold it to answer anyone that questions your authority.*

Chapter 3

SIGNING UP FOR THE FUTURE

You've stirred up the anthill by taking your parent to the doctor and getting all your siblings involved. Now, you have to take action on what you've started. You need to get your parent's legal papers in order so you can protect their future and control some of the events heading their way.

Consider sitting down with your parent and talking to them about granting you Power of Attorney or setting up a Trust, Living Will, and Will. If they have assets, you may want to protect them by visiting a lawyer experienced in safeguarding assets. These aren't easy things to discuss. Funeral/memorial services and burial requests are even more daunting subjects. But if you don't talk about this soon, you may miss the opportunity. These legal papers have to be signed while your parent is still competent. Asset protection usually should be completed five years before your parent goes into a nursing home. If your parent is having any trouble, that window of opportunity can quickly close, if and when they're rendered incompetent. If that happens, you'll need to go before a judge to obtain conservatorship (or an adult guardianship).

Conservatorship

A conservatorship grants you the right to make medical and financial decisions on your parent's behalf. To act as someone's legal guardian or conservator, you must petition for guardianship and go to court to have your parent declared incompetent based on findings from a medical expert. If your parent is ruled incompetent and you appear a suitable guardian, the court then transfers the responsibility to you. You will manage finances, living arrangements, medical decisions, or any combination of these tasks for your parent.

This process often takes a good deal of time and money. If family members disagree about the need for guardianship, the process can become especially contentious, prolonged, and costly.

Having your parent sign a Power of Attorney form is necessary while they are cognizant and able to make a decision on their own. However, asking your parent to give you, or someone in your family, Power of Attorney over their affairs (both financial and health) might surprise or even anger them. They may not be ready for it. Heck, you may not be ready for it. But it's crucial to set this up as soon as possible. It must be done while your parent is competent and capable of making informed decisions.

A good way to begin is to have a heart-to-heart talk with your parent. Tell them why they need to visit a lawyer and get some particular forms filled out and signed. You might want to include your family members in this discussion. There's persuasive power in numbers. Make sure your family members understand why you need to do this so they can back you up if your parent puts up an argument. Have them read this chapter, or Google, using search terms such as:

Elderly parents making poor decisions

How much does it cost to get guardianship?

What happens if you are declared mentally incompetent?

Trusts, Wills, and Power of Attorney

According to a 2017 survey by Princeton Survey Research Associates International, 80% of people over 72 indicated that they already had a Will or Living Trust. Your parent may already have one also. It doesn't hurt to ask. If they have assets, they'll need to protect them. If they don't, they should at least have a Will/Power of Attorney set up so that someone in your family can be appointed to take charge if they're incapacitated. Someone from your family needs to make sure. A simple Will assures where their assets will go, but a court-appointed conservator will have to oversee the process.

In contrast, a Living Trust places all the assets inside the Trust. It has an appointed executor (usually a family member or trusted friend appointed by your parent) to oversee and carry out the requests of the Will. It also protects your parent's beneficiaries from taxes and public announcements that are part of probate proceedings.

You may have to explain to your parent why it's so essential for them to put their wishes for their future care on paper and appoint someone to take charge once they're unable to.

But the Living Trust is not all you'll need. Be sure you have a Power of Attorney for Health Care and Durable Power of Attorney. These documents are usually included in the Living Trust. When my brother-in-law first mentioned that my mother's cheap Living Trust lacked these two documents, my sister and I gave him a blank stare. Mom had already set up her Living Trust. We figured that was all she needed. At that time, neither of us truly understood the significance of having our mother sign the Power of Attorney for Health Care and Durable Power of Attorney papers. Be sure that your Living Trust includes these two vital documents.

Like many people, we didn't realize how critical those forms would be in caring for her future needs. When Mom questioned us about whether they were necessary, we waffled. We didn't have a good explanation for why she really needed it. She, in turn, didn't want to sign the forms we'd put before her. It took us six months to get her comfortable with the idea. By that time, her health had deteriorated, and she was starting to show signs of dementia.

Shortly after my mom signed those papers, she was admitted to the hospital for an emergency operation. We needed a signed Power of Attorney for Health Care to decide her care. While she was hospitalized, we also found out that she had set up a new bank account outside of her Trust and directed her pension payments to be sent to this new account. It took our Power of Attorney form to unravel this mess so we could continue to pay her bills while she recovered from surgery. We were thankful that she finally agreed to sign the Power of Attorney for Health Care and Durable Power of Attorney forms, and they were notarized and ready to use when we needed them. Without them, we may have needed to go to court for conservatorship to take over her affairs. It would have involved a lawyer, money, and time. Each state has slightly different laws in regards to the Power of Attorney. But I learned the hard way that it's imperative to have those documents signed and ready for when you'll need them.

 ## Don't Put Off Important Decisions

Take your parent to see a lawyer and have everything taken care of at one time. If you put off getting legal forms signed and helping your parent set up a Will or Trust, you may regret it later. Here are the primary documents you'll need:

- **Power of Attorney for Health Care**: This form names the person responsible for making health care decisions and carrying out the Life Directives as written. Hospital doctors and nurses will suddenly listen to you when you present this form.

- **Life Directive-Living Will**: This is a plan with instructions on how your parent wants to be cared for should they become incapacitated or rendered incompetent to make decisions regarding their health care. It usually includes a clause stating that they do or do not wish to be kept alive by artificial methods should the doctors determine that they have no chance of recovery. It may also include their wishes for organ donation.

- **Death Directive**: This states their preference regarding the disposal of their remains once they have passed on. It should say whether they want a conventional burial, cremation or if they want to donate their body to science. They may also include the type of funeral or memorial service they prefer and provide details of how they want their wishes carried out by the family.

- **Trust and/or Will**: Each state has its own limit, but as a rule-of-thumb, if your parent has any liquid assets or real property, they should establish a Trust and name someone reliable as the executor of the Trust (it can be sibling, friend or an attorney). A comprehensive Trust can include Advance Directives and Power of Attorney. If your parent doesn't need a Trust, they should have a Will drawn up stating how they want their property distributed and naming an executor to carry out their wishes. Some states, such as California, may have laws that combine Medical Power of Attorney and a Living Will into a single document. In California's case, it's called an Advance Health Care Directive.

Asset Protection

Protecting your parent's assets can save them thousands should they eventually need long-term care. According to a 2015 statistic by the Family Caregiver Alliance, among elders aged 65 years or older, 69% will develop disabilities before they die, and 35% will eventually enter a nursing home. Nursing homes typically cost around $100,000 a year and may take a significant bite out of your parent's nest egg. Consulting with a lawyer for Trust advice is often a prudent step for asset protection. Lawyers, especially those specializing in estate planning, will inform you and your parent of many options for protecting their assets.

Estate laws can be complex. If you don't know anyone specializing in Trusts, check with your local senior center. Also, check your local Yelp ratings and carefully read the reviews—especially the bad ones. You can also go to the American Bar Association (www.americanbar.org) to get a referral in your state for a Trust lawyer. The Association helps to hold lawyers to high standards. If you have an accountant or family attorney, you can also ask them for referrals for a Trust lawyer.

If you are referred from your local American Bar Association, your first lawyer visit is free (as of this writing). To find a specialist lawyer, Google *American Bar Association Referral Service*. It will refer you to several lawyers in your area. Do some online research and find one you prefer. Check where they graduated from law school and what clients they commonly work for.

If your parent has assets worth less than $35,000 and no property, consider having them set up a joint checking account with your name on it. Then you'll at least be able to pay their bills if they become incapacitated. Either that or have them sign over Power of Attorney so that you can help them pay their bills and make medical decisions if they are unable to.

Trusts

If your parent has assets or real property they'd like to protect, such as a house or land, they may want to think about setting up a Trust. Otherwise, all their assets may have to go through probate when they die. A Trust is an alternative to the probate process that will save the estate (and you) a considerable amount of money in court fees, legal costs, and taxes. A Trust allows you (if you are an appointed trustee or executor) to access and control your parent's assets so that you can continue to pay their expenses when they are unable to. Most often, an attorney is needed when there is a Trust. They can also offer a buffer between the family and the assigned executor.

 ## Probate

Probate is a legal process in which the named executor (usually a family member who has to hire a lawyer) goes before a court and identifies and catalogs all of your parent's properties, has the properties appraised, pays all debts and taxes, proves that your parent's Will is legally valid, and then distributes the inheritance to you and the other heirs following the instructions in the Will. This process can take up to six months and can easily involve thousands of dollars in legal fees. If your parent owns land in another state, you'll need to go through a separate probate process in that state. The probate process is also part of the public record. This means everyone will know your hardship, and solicitors will fly in like vultures, selling life insurance, investment schemes, and burial plots.

All of your parent's assets, including their bank accounts, are in the executor's hands during the probate period. This person pays the bills, mortgage payments, doctor and hospital bills, burial costs, and extensive lawyer fees until the probate process is complete.

Setting up a Trust

To avoid probate, I recommend you consult an estate lawyer who can set up a Living Trust, Power of Attorney for both Durable and Health Care, and a Will at the same time. Every state has its own rules and guidelines on Trusts and Power of Attorney. A lawyer will know the laws in each state and can draw up all the papers quickly and accurately. Some lawyers advertise their specialized service in setting up Trusts for low prices, but they may not be the best for your needs if your parent has many assets.

Trust lawyers usually charge a percentage-based fee, based on assets. If your parent has considerable assets, a Living Trust can ensure the best financial outcomes. Most people pay a lawyer to set up their Trusts, like paying a mechanic to take care of their car. Like a car, a Trust requires occasional maintenance. You can do it yourself if you have the time and know-how. Unfortunately, most of us don't have the time or energy to keep up with current tax laws and ensure everything is done correctly.

Trust lawyers I've spoken to claim that the most significant problems they face are Trusts that are improperly set up or poorly maintained. Things such as appointing a proper successor trustee or correctly funding the Trust can be much less of a hassle with competent estate attorneys. They can help you keep informed and keep your documents up-to-date.

If you're entirely against lawyers or think they are too costly, there's an excellent book put out by Nolo Publishing called *Make Your Own Living Trust* that's available for less than $40 (as of this writing). Although written by a lawyer, it's easy to read and understand. It contains the necessary forms you'll need to make a legal Trust. Nolo Publishing (www.nolo.com) also has books on estate planning and avoiding probate you might want to look at. They're easy to read, and some come with software and ready-to-fill forms.

Quicken has gotten into the Trust business with Nolo Publishing. It offers a software program that lets you write your own Trust and Will based on a series of questions and answers. The premium version appears to have the Power of Attorney forms you'll need. It's currently available on Amazon, Costco, and practically everywhere. If your parent doesn't have significant assets and doesn't need a complex Living Trust, this may be an inexpensive way to go.

My mother always tried to keep her financial affairs in good order. Her mom had died without a Will, and Mom saw the chaos and backbiting between her many siblings. So, Mom had a Trust drawn up long before my sister and I knew about it. The only problem was that she had it done by a lawyer she found in one of those little ads in the newspaper. It didn't cost her much, but it didn't include a Power of Attorney and wasn't maintained. To maintain a Trust, your parent has to make sure all new assets are added to the Trust and *not* their own name. It seems like an easy task, but it's really easy to forget about that Living Trust once it's tucked away and they get on with life.

One of her most important assets, a property she purchased after she created the Trust, was never placed inside her Trust. When Mom died, my sister and I had access to her assets *–except* for that parcel of land. It cost us about 25 percent of the land's appraised value to transfer it to our names. We could have avoided that had she placed that land in her Living Trust when she bought it.

Types of Trusts

There are many types of Trusts for different needs. The most common and easiest to set up is a Living Trust. This Trust, created during your parent's lifetime, renames assets and holds them under the Trust where they're protected from probate.

When the Trust is established, your parent must designate a successor to serve as trustee or executor. This should be an efficient, reliable individual who will get things done and carry out their wishes as written in their Will and Power of Attorney. A trustee or executor will open Trust accounts when necessary to pay doctor bills, house payments, or buy groceries for them when they can't. The Trust becomes a third-party entity for managing the assets. When your parent dies, you have no need for probate because all of your parent's assets and property were listed, categorized, appraised, and in the Trust. But property may have to be re-appraised if estate tax or the property's value affects distribution. The Trust contents are then distributed according to the Will included in the Trust records.

Living Trusts are usually revocable and changeable as long as your parent is alive. There are also Irrevocable Trusts. Unlike a Living Trust, an Irrevocable Trust cannot be changed without the permission of the beneficiaries. Placing your parent's assets in an Irrevocable Trust protects them from creditors but takes away their control. However, they can be exempt from nursing home costs, as of this writing.

Specialized Trusts

Specialized trusts exist for shielding assets for a variety of situations. Here are just a few:

- **Marital and Bypass Trusts (also known as A/B Trusts).** These legal arrangements allow married couples to avoid estate tax on certain assets when one spouse passes away. Upon death, the estate's assets are split into two separate Trusts. Think of them as Above and Below. A = Above ground. B = Below ground. In setting up A/B Trusts, you almost always set up a single Initial Trust that is revocable. This Initial Trust ends at the death of either partner and is split into new Trusts

(A and B). Upon this death, the trustee (usually the surviving spouse) divides the property from the Initial Trust and places some into the A Trust and some into the B Trust. The B Trust usually pays income to the survivor and passes the principal to children and grandchildren. The tax goal of the B Trust is to get this money out of the couple's combined estate so it escapes estate taxation after the second spouse's death. An A/B Trust can be useful when there are significant assets to protect.

- **Special-Needs Trusts.** This Trust is used to set up assets for a loved one, such as a disabled child, who cannot care for their needs and is receiving public assistance. It allows them to receive an inheritance from the trustee without affecting their Supplemental Security Income or Medicaid benefits.

- **Qualified Terminable Interest Property (QTIP).** This is like an A/B Trust, except the surviving spouse cannot change the portion of the estate directed to the children. This type of Trust is often used to guarantee an income to a surviving spouse but still pass the estate on to the children of a previous marriage. The QTIP Trust provides for the surviving spouse. When the surviving spouse dies, the children receive the remaining assets as directed by the first spouse.

- **Charitable Remainder Trusts.** This is an Irrevocable Trust that allows some or all assets to go to a charity. Sometimes the Trust recipient receives income from the Trust until they die, then the remaining assets go to a charity. They can also have a portion go to their children or other heirs. When the heirs die, the remaining assets go to the charity of the trustee's choice. Eventually, some or all of the assets end up going to charity.

- **Irrevocable Life Insurance Trusts.** This Trust protects the death payment in life insurance policies from estate taxes. The life insurance is placed in an Irrevocable Trust, where the insured names their heirs as the beneficiaries. The death payment remains in the Trust when the insured dies, where the beneficiaries can draw from it tax-free.

HELPING YOUR AGING PARENT

A Trust is probably your parent's best first step in asset protection. For more involved asset protection, have your parent check with their Trust lawyer. Help them prepare a list of questions that pertain to the subject of their assets.

Does Your Parent Need a Trust?

If your parent has real property, a business, or assets, they should consider a Living Trust. Here are a few more reasons a Trust is prudent:

- **To avoid probate in another state.** If your parent has property in another state, you can avoid dealing with different probate regulations with a Trust.

- **Confidentiality.** With a Living Trust, there is no public record of the proceeding.

- **To protect assets in case of incapacitation.** If you anticipate that your parent may not be capable of managing their finances in the future, an assigned successor trustee can manage the Trust. In some cases, that can be you or one of your family members who will manage the Trust if a physical or mental illness prevents your parent from being able to do it. This protects them from unscrupulous relatives or friends who might exploit their illness and take their wealth.

- **To protect your parent's business.** Without a Trust, your parent's business could enter legal limbo while the court decides its fate. Meanwhile, creditors are charging interest, employees' livelihoods may be at stake, and the estate assets shrink.

Who Doesn't Need a Trust?

Is a Trust always needed? Here are a couple of reasons your parent might avoid setting up a trust:

- As Bob Dylan once said in a song, "when you ain't got nothing, you got nothing to lose." Not everyone has a lot of assets. Probate fees are typically a percentage of the estate. If your parent's estate (all their material wealth) is less than $25,000, setting up a Trust may not be worth the expense. It might cost more than you would have to spend on probate. In many states, small estates are even exempt from probate. The laws change, as does the amount residents can leave to their heirs without going through probate. If your parent doesn't own a home or other real property and doesn't have other significant assets, you can just set up a joint bank account to pay their bills for them. When they die, the money in the bank account will automatically be yours. Your parent may get along fine with just a simple Will. (You'll still need the Power of Attorney to make decisions for them.)

- If your parent doesn't own property but has money in life insurance policies, individual retirement accounts, and other contractual plans that already designate a beneficiary, they may not need a Trust. Again, you just need a joint bank account or Power of Attorney to help pay their bills and represent them when they cannot represent themselves.

 ## Once in a Trust, Always in a Trust

Once your parent sets up a Living Trust, make sure they don't change banks. My mother did and had her retirement checks direct deposited into that new account. If the account at the new bank isn't set up as a Trust account, you're not going to be able to get access to the money without a Power of Attorney (unless the account is in a joint account with your name). Your parent may not need your help right away, but eventually, you may need to buy groceries or pay doctors' bills using the money in their checking or savings account.

Also, if they buy or inherit any additional land or real property after setting up a Trust, they must sign the title to the property into the Trust. Otherwise, if the property is outside the Trust, you'll have to pay a lawyer and go through probate proceedings to get the title to that property when they die—even if they had a Trust. Make sure that everything is in the name of the Trust.

HELPING YOUR AGING PARENT

Power of Attorney for Health Care

An estate lawyer can set up a Health Care Directive, which can be a Power of Attorney for Health Care (sometimes called the Medical Power of Attorney) and Durable Power of Attorney at the same time. The lawyer will customize the forms for your parent's needs and ensure that they satisfy the legal requirements of the state your parent resides in.

Even if your parent doesn't have a Trust, it's vital to set up the Power of Attorney forms. Each state has different rules and its own specialized documents. You can purchase generic forms for Power of Attorney for Health Care at office supply stores or websites like Rocket Lawyer (www.rocketlawyer.com). You buy this form, fill it in, and have your parent sign it before a public notary. Have your parent keep the original and make a notarized copy for yourself. Find out if it's necessary to have witnesses at the signing as well. If you ever get an emergency call in the middle of the night, you're be deputized to make decisions on their care. When life and death decisions are necessary, you'll wear that Power of Attorney for Healthcare like a badge and hold it to answer anyone that questions your authority.

Have this signed form ready before your parent is unconscious in the emergency room or becomes mentally incapacitated. If you have family members close by and willing to help, you may feel it's best to have their names listed. Most lawyers recommend that only one person in the family be the one to make the critical health care decisions, and they suggest this from experience. The most level-headed and responsible person is the best choice to sign these forms. Make sure your parent agrees with your recommendation.

Durable Power of Attorney for Finances

This form names the person responsible for caring for your parent's legal and financial needs if, or when, they're incapacitated. This person is authorized to sign checks and documents, enter into contracts, and otherwise act as your parent's legal agent.

Again, you can have a lawyer draw up a Durable Power of Attorney, or you can buy the generic forms for your state online. Here are some sites to get started:

- Rocket Lawyer (www.rocketlawyer.com)
- Law Depot (www.lawdepot.com)
- Legal Zoom (www.legalzoom.com)

This isn't an easy form for many parents to sign. They often feel like they're giving you the power to take over their life. You can assure them that this isn't the case. All the Durable Power of Attorney means is that they have legally "deputized" you to care for their needs if they're unable to. These duties include writing checks to pay bills, buying essentials, entering into contracts, managing properties, and filing taxes.

Signing this power over to someone is difficult for most independent seniors. It sure was for my mother. And, like me, you may feel uncomfortable asking for Durable Power of Attorney over your parent's affairs. But when you need it, that form will open doors for you. When my mother's health began to fail, we were able to step in, hold things together financially, and take care of her. Again, your parent must sign this form and have it notarized while competent to make such decisions. Don't delay.

If You Don't Have a Durable Power of Attorney

A lawyer will file a petition with the court to interview specialists regarding your parent's competency. A lawyer will be assigned to represent your parent. If your parent is declared incompetent, the court will appoint a legal guardian to control your parent's affairs. You'll be petitioning that they name you as guardian. Fees for all this are deducted from the estate. It's a time-consuming and emotionally draining experience—especially if your parent insists that they are competent and decides to fight. It's best to do everything you can to convince your parent before this happens.

Living Wills are usually part of the Living Trust, regulated by state requirements, and have strict guidelines for handling, storing, and activating them. The terms in these documents can be broad and complicated.

The lawyer who sets this up often takes the wording from a generic version. You have to read it very carefully. Help your parent define their wishes before visiting that lawyer. It'll be easier for you to carry out these decisions if you've discussed them with your parents. Use the sample questions below as a guide to clarify what your parent wants. Then have the lawyer draft these specific requests into the Living Will instead of using a generic form that may be garbled with legalese.

Critical Questions to Ask for a Life Directive

How do you define "artificial means"?

☐ a machine respirator ☐ a heart pump ☐ a feeding tube

☐ a colostomy tube ☐ a hydration tube

How long do you wish to be kept alive by artificial means?

☐ 12 hours ☐ 24 hours ☐ 3 days ☐ 1 week ☐ 1 month ☐ 6 months

☐ As long as I can afford it.

Do you want to be resuscitated if your heart fails?

☐ yes ☐ no ☐ It depends on the chances of full recovery.

Would you like your organs to be donated?

☐ yes ☐ no ☐ Some (listed below)

Other notes: _____

_____

Figure 3-1 *Critical Questions for a Life Directive*

Having a clear Life Directive from your parent makes it easier to carry out their wishes when the inevitable time comes. It also helps avoid arguments among family members, decreases feelings of guilt, and defines the appropriate actions you should follow at the final stage of your parent's life. It's essential to have a detailed directive from your parent. There's no room for ambiguity. If your parent doesn't want to be kept alive by artificial means, have them specify what "artificial means" they're referring to. Is it a respirator? Is it a heart pump? Is it a colostomy tube? Is it a feeding tube? What exactly do they mean?

Sometimes there's a need for someone to be kept alive by artificial means. They may have to be on a respirator following surgery, for example. Once on the respirator, if things go wrong, how long should they remain on the respirator? Tensions run high when loved ones are unwell. Have your parent specify when they want to be removed from artificial life support systems now. Then you won't have to be the one making the extremely difficult life or death decision while your family is arguing over it. Eventually, the hospital bill for keeping them alive in a vegetative state will start to weigh on your decision.

My mother didn't want to be kept alive by artificial means, which scared us when she needed an operation for diverticulitis. During this major operation, they removed a large part of her intestine. She was put on a respirator for 48 hours and a feeding tube for months. Was I in violation of her request? Did I violate her directive by keeping her alive through artificial means? Probably, but I thought she had a good chance at recovering, which she did.

The feeding tube came out, and she was able to enjoy a few more precious months of life with us. After that, I was satisfied with my decision, and so was she. Sometimes, as an executor, you have to make the call on the finer points in a Living Will or Health Directive. It's never a simple decision, but your parent can make it easier when the instructions are clear and not vague.

Directives offer guidelines that your parent sets up and puts you in charge to follow. You're left to enforce the finer points of those wishes. Your own discretion may play a role in how you interpret the guidelines. Life isn't always as simple as what is written on a directive, but your parent's wishes should be as clear as possible.

Death Directives and Last Requests

What will happen to your parent's mortal body when their life ends? Do they want to be cremated and their ashes scattered at sea or dropped from a plane over some particular site? Do they want to be buried in the family plot in the Ozarks or next to a loved one in Hollywood? Do they want to donate their body to science?

My mother never talked to us about death. Much to our surprise, my aunt told us that Mom wanted her ashes scattered in the bay at Monterey, CA. My sister and I obeyed. We rented a two-person kayak and paddled out beyond the swells. Although we had some rough surf and a few boats to contend with, our private service for our mother was carried out in a beautiful and bittersweet way. It is a touching memory.

We'll get into services and last rites in more detail in Chapter 8. But so that you're prepared, *Figure 3-2* is an Informal Death Directive, which should give you clear instructions as to what, how, and where your parent would like their remains disposed of. Bear in mind you may not be able to fulfill all their requests due to monetary and legal considerations. Not all states will let you throw your parent's ashes into the wind or drop them from a plane. But at least you'll have their request in writing so you can carry out the spirit of what they wanted. When the time comes, you can bring one of your parent's last requests to life.

Informal Death Directive

It is my last request that when I die, my body:

☐ be buried at _____

☐ be buried with my _____

☐ be cremated and my ashes _____

☐ be donated to science
   (Facility/university preferred) _____

It is my last request that when I die, my body: *(continued)*

☐ _____

At my funeral/memorial service, I would like:

_____

_____

_____

_____

_____

Upon my death, please send notice to the following people:

Name _____ Contact info _____

Name _____ Contact info _____

Name _____ Contact info _____

Name _____ Contact info _____

Name _____ Contact info _____

Name _____ Contact info _____

Name _____ Contact info _____

I give full responsibility to _____ to enable
this directive. By doing so they will be fulfilling my last request.

Signed _____ Date _____

Witnessed by _____ Date _____

Figure 3-2 *Death Directive and Last Request*

Preparing these directives and getting them signed is part of planning for your parent's future and the end of their life. This should be done with love and consideration for their feelings and fears. Ask if your parent wants to talk with you about any worries. Death is a part of life, and fears are normal. Getting their fears out in the open could be a way for you to help your parent overcome them. Let them know what an important significance they've had upon your life. Old age is a time for introspection on life. It's not going to be easy for you either, and honesty helps everyone accept what's inevitable and come to terms. By being open, you'll also gain their trust.

While you're having these discussions, it might be a good time to ask them what they'd like for people to remember about them. Bring up the fact that you might have to eventually write an obituary for them. What would they want you to include? Maybe they've already written one. Consult the Personal Information Fact Sheet in *Figure 3-3* for some facts you might want to add. You don't have to use "obituary" if it seems morbid. Tell your parent you want to get all their "life information" together. Make it a positive experience—find out about all the peaks in their life—the best times, their favorite memories, how it felt to be honored by their peers, and what they felt the important events were.

Right after your parent's death, your emotions are strained while making arrangements and preparing for the funeral or memorial service. It's a real challenge to get all this information together, especially the sequences of events. One of the nicest things you can do for your parents is honor their life with a beautiful obituary published online or in their local newspaper. But that's very difficult to do when you're grieving and can't remember the significant events of their life. Let your parent help you prepare this fact sheet while they're still alive. How I wish I had done this!

Personal Information Fact Sheet

Name _____ Nickname _____

Birth date _____ Birthplace _____

Moved to Current Location (date) _____ from _____

Married to whom _____

_____

Education

High School _____ College _____

Degrees or Scholastic Achievements _____

_____

Occupations _____

_____

Awards/ Achievements/ Recognitions _____

Retired from _____

Personal Activities
Church/Clubs/Fraternities _____

_____

Hobbies _____

Favorite Travel Destinations _____

_____

_____

Favorite Saying/Quote _____

_____

_____

Favorite Memory _____

_____

_____

Philosophy or mission statement on life _____

_____

_____

Important passions _____

_____

_____

Figure 3-3 *Personal Information Fact Sheet*

While you're at it, have your parent add you as a "Legacy Contact" on Facebook if they have a Facebook or social media account. That way, if something should happen to them, you can control their account, report on them, or use it as a Memoriam should they die. It also makes it easier for you to delete the account. Also, make sure that your parent offers you a list of their e-mail account passwords. You'll need them when you need to close their accounts eventually.

Reward Yourself

After all legal documents are filled out, signed, notarized, and witnessed, make sure your parent stores the documents in a place you can find and access them. If your parent is forgetful, you may want to keep a copy for yourself. You can always digitize it and store it on GoogleDocs or your preferred cloud storage system.

Once you get all these legal papers taken care of, treat everyone to dinner. We took Mom to her favorite Italian restaurant. I swear her eyes glowed in the soft light of the candles as she ordered her favorite Brasato al vino. We needed a reward for dealing with the tensions and hassle of getting through the legal and mental morass. This is one of the most challenging steps in your parent's care because you have to push so much to get it done, and it's so important. The rest of the steps covered in this book will fall into place when you get over these legal hurdles. Many will even come about of their own accord. By taking care of the legal planning, you'll help secure your parent's and your own future.

 ## Unfinished Business with Siblings

It never fails that one sibling will have made a private business deal with your parent that seems unfair or misguided to the others. You may have to bite your cheek and forgive that for now, though the resentment may simmer and fester long after your parent is gone. Sometimes, there are no records of these arrangements, and you may not find out about them until your parent has died and all the assets are settled. There's often nothing you can do other than litigation which is often not worth the expense and hassle. For your own sanity, it's often best to let it go and get on with life.

If You're Stuck

Don't give up if your parent digs in their heels and refuses to grant you Durable Power of Attorney or deal with any of your attempts to help them. Be patient. It may take some time for them to get used to the idea. They may not trust lawyers, or you, or any other family member to handle their affairs. But to take your parent to court to battle it out for control of their finances is lengthy, costly, and usually, a lose-lose situation that tears families apart. It's something that you probably don't want to get into.

You'll probably feel frustrated if you've tried your best argument, tried peer pressure and family pressure, and your parent is still too stubborn to listen. You could inform them of the long and lengthy probate process and how hefty lawyer fees will gobble up most of what they might want to pass on to their family. Try to reason with them and offer them some time to think it over. Find it in your heart to forgive them. Accept them for who they are, not who you want them to be. Don't give up on your efforts. Eventually, they'll probably come around. Most people are realistic about their own finality and will be happy to help a responsible child they trust.

Some of these retirement homes are
like cruise ships on land.

Chapter 4

HOUSING OPTIONS

As your parent grows older, their caregiving needs increase. If you're helping them fulfill these needs, you may come to a point where you realize you have limitations on your ability to care for them. Especially if you have a career or family, live far from your parent, or cannot always be there for them on an as-needed basis. How do you introduce a change, like the idea of alternate housing options? How can you explain to them all the housing options available in a way that won't overwhelm them?

With my mother, she seemed happy living in her modest mobile home. She never complained, but I think she did become tired of cooking for herself. She never enjoyed preparing food anyway. On every visit, I noticed she was eating more and more of her meals from a can. I also noticed that maintaining the small yard around her mobile home was beginning to stress her. Only a few years before, she enjoyed yard work.

Honestly, I felt depressed by the worsening conditions of her surroundings when I visited. Her home was dark, illuminated only by the light of the ever-blaring television.

I'd come by on weekends to help her with chores and we'd chat, but most of my days were taken up with work and my own family's activities.

Truthfully, I could have spent more time with her.

When she started complaining about her neighbors, it gave me an extra incentive to examine other housing options. My sister and I worked together to find a place that offered plenty of opportunities to make new friends and socialize. Knowing that she didn't like to cook, we searched for an alternative that provided dining experiences to replace her lonely dinner out of a can. That perked her interest, so starting from this, we began our search on the many housing options available for older people.

We started by searching the Internet, looking for retirement homes, apartments, and other housing options. It took us weeks before we had a few choices to present to Mom. Soon we were visiting dozens of retirement homes, apartments, and private housing options with her in tow. It took a while before finding what we thought would be a good fit. Those days were long, but I'm glad we spent the time. Mom enjoyed being with us and even called us by our childhood nicknames like we were small. It also gave my sister and me a chance to work together helping Mom.

Searching for new housing for your parent involves four choices:

1. Can they, or the family, afford the place that offers the level of care they need?

2. Are they mentally receptive to the idea of moving?

3. Can you help them find a place they are likely to be happier?

4. Is the level of care at the new facility suitable for their needs?

You may be the one encouraging the move if you notice your parent requiring more care. But a doctor or geriatric advisor may also recommend moving if, during a physical exam, they see a decline in your parent's ability to keep up with life and adequately care for themselves. They may recommend a combination of the following:

• Volunteers who will make home visits several days each week.

• Several days at the senior center each week to get more social activity.

- A private apartment in a senior community where meals are prepared, dishes are washed, maintenance is done, and exciting social and cultural activities are planned.

- A nursing home or private residential care facility.

As long as your parent can make decisions, the final choice on where they live is theirs. When it comes to making the move, letting them be the key contributor in the decision process assures they'll be happier with the changes.

I learned the hard way to never assume you know the best place for your parent to live. If they want to move into a dilapidated trailer park rather than into your new granny flat, as my mom did, you have to respect their rationale. As long as they are competent to make decisions, you're the facilitator or negotiator, not the decision-maker. You can always point out the downside of their decision if they are enamored with something that seems impractical—as they did with your ideas growing up.

Option 1: Moving Your Parent in with You

Some families move their parents into their own homes with them so they can look after them. If you have a good relationship with your parent, an extra room in your home, the time and desire to look after them, you may consider this option. Caring for your parent can be one of the most rewarding, and sometimes one of the most brutally challenging things, you can do in a lifetime. The proximity and time you'll have with your parent will either bring you closer or tear you apart.

Minor Improvements May Be All You Need

If you decide to take care of your parent in your own home, making minor upgrades to your home for an elderly or disabled person isn't that difficult. An extra grab bar in the bathroom and a railing to help your parent up the front steps may be all that is needed. Beyond these things, you'll want to consider clutter, slippery throw rugs, and cramped spaces that increase fall risk. Check for a home safety evaluation in your area or download the free

"Check for Safety" booklet from the CDC on their website at STEADI— Older Adult Fall Prevention (https://www.cdc.gov/steadi/patient.html).

Building a Granny Flat

If you don't have room inside your home for another person, consider adding a granny flat or a new bedroom and bathroom. A 400-square-foot granny flat with a bedroom, bathroom, heater, stove, cabinets, and flooring can probably be built on your lot, depending on the location and style of construction. First, consult your local zoning authorities at City Hall. Some areas don't allow ADUs, or "Additional Dwelling Units," while other regions actually encourage them. Some communities even offer low-interest construction loans and financial assistance for building an ADU. Find out if financial aid is available for family hardship dwellings or ADUs. Often, you can get back much of the money you put into the additional unit when you sell your home. And who knows, someday after your parent passes on, you can use it as a rental for extra money or as housing for a teenage son or daughter you may want a little distance from.

Finding a contractor who specializes in granny flats isn't difficult. They should be familiar with how high the grab bars should be above the toilet and any other ADA building requirements. The best contractor can often be found by word of mouth, as most of them stay in business because of their reputation. For ideas, check out the book, *In-laws, Outlaws, and Granny Flats: Your Guide to Turning One House into Two Homes.*

Make sure that you involve your parent in the project. You might want them to choose the carpets or drapes and the interior colors within the three choices that you've approved. The more they feel the place is theirs, the happier they're likely to be staying there.

How Well Will You Really Get Along?

Will your parent be happier living near you than living alone or somewhere else? Are you able to be there for them? Consider carefully if the two of you will be able to fit into each other's lifestyle. Does your parent require a lot of attention? If you have younger children, will they get along? Will your spouse be able to tolerate your parent in your home or near your home? How about after a year or two?

Each family is different. Moving a parent in with you usually requires more adjustment than just some remodeling or adding a room or granny flat to your current house. It often involves a change of lifestyle focused on caring for your parent. Can you fit their caregiving with your career, family, and present life? If not, it's wise to be honest with yourself. There are other options to consider below.

Moving your parent in with you may seem complicated, but it can also be rewarding. It can be a rare opportunity to do something good for another person—the same person that once made many sacrifices for you.

 ## Possible Tax Breaks for a Parent Living with You

Income tax rules change yearly, so please consult the most current IRS rules. As of this writing, there are a few possible tax breaks.

- **Dependent Parent:** According to IRS criteria, a parent living with you may make you eligible for a $500 federal tax break if they are your "dependent."

- **Care Credit:** If your parent cannot care for themselves and you pay someone to care for them so you can work, you might qualify for a credit representing a portion of the costs.

- **Unreimbursed Bills:** If you paid and weren't reimbursed for your parent's hospital, medical or dental bills, you might be able to deduct the cost from your taxes.

Not every family is emotionally suited to live in close proximity. This is why my mom chose not to move into my new granny flat. We weren't comfortable being so close. If this is the story in your family, it's unlikely that you or your parent will change at this late stage, even if you might like to. Your parent will still want their independence, even if they need a walker or a wheelchair. Fortunately, there are other housing options available.

Option 2: Have Someone Come to Your Parent (Aging in Place)

If your parent needs minimal care, you can arrange to have someone look in on or after them in their home. The cost depends on the frequency of visits and the participant's skill level. Night and weekend care may cost more. Having in-home care may even cost less than moving them to a retirement home, depending on the amount of care required.

You may see home care being advertised on television. Ask your doctor or a professional geriatric care manager to find a home-visit care service. They may save you the cost of their fee by providing you with help in applying for Medicare benefits and finding less-expensive resources and help for your parent. You can also find many home care agencies listed online.

Home-health care agencies can provide personnel to help with general chores such as bathing, eating, dressing, and toileting. Sometimes these agencies will charge your parent, and sometimes they may be partially funded by the state you reside in. Some are sponsored by religious organizations. Most professional care agencies vet their employees before they hire them. You may want to ask about their vetting policies for your peace of mind. You can also check the references and credentials of an applicant yourself by going online.

Tips for Hiring In-Home Care

- Interview each candidate in person.
- Communicate the specific needs of your parent to the care provider.
- Discuss compensation and payment schedules.
- Request references and contact them.
- Perform background checks by calling and checking online.
- Don't be afraid to move on if the person is not the right fit.

If professional health care is needed, you might consider live-in nurses to provide one-on-one care. A live-in nurse might cost as much or more as it would cost to have your parent stay in a nursing home, but it's an option that will let your parent remain in their own home. A good live-in nurse can provide top-notch care if you or your parent can afford it.

Does Medicare Pay for Home Health Visits?

In some cases, Medicare will pay for at-home care. But there are restrictions. Here are a few:

- Your parent's doctor has to arrange and set up your parent's home health care plan. Your parent's condition has to, according to the doctor, require skilled nursing care. Cooking and bathing may not be considered "medical" care.

- Their doctor needs to certify that they are homebound. Your parent must have a disability that would require considerable effort to attend in-person health care services.

- Medicare will not pay for full-time nursing care but usually pays for home care visits if the visits are intermittent skilled nursing care or therapy. Ask if Medicare has certified the home health agency. That means that the provider has met the requirements to receive Medicare payments. Medicare certification is one way to protect you and assure the quality of your care. Visit the Medicare website (www.medicare.gov) and click on "Find Healthcare Providers."

Roommate

While not for everyone, there is also the possibility of finding a roommate for your parent. This can be a viable option, especially if they own their home and have an extra bedroom or two and are looking for companionship, or a little extra money. There may be a person your parent's age or a little younger in the community who is looking for shared housing. Placing an ad on the bulletin board at your local senior center, local community college, or even in the local newspaper might bring you a surprising number of applicants. A sample rental application can be found for your state with a quick online search. Ensure the applicant signs the bottom line, giving you permission to check their references. Call the previous landlord as they are likely to provide an accurate reference.

Don't Discriminate

When placing ads for roommates or live-ins, it can be tempting to tailor your ad to attract a specific type of roommate. Gender or racial discrimination is a sensitive subject. Never dismiss a potential renter because of your own gender, age, or racial preferences. Interview all applicants with the same amount of respect, no matter how they may appear to you. Let them provide you with a completed application and make your judgment based on their qualifications and references.

First-time impressions can be deceiving. When vetting new applicants, try and apply your rational and emotional mind in your decision-making. You should look for a compassionate person your parent can get along with and someone who has a proven record of responsible behavior.

If you've found someone you feel would make an exceptional roommate, conduct a credit check, background check, and check the sex offender registry. This will cost you, but it will provide factual information about the person. It will indicate if they're financially mature enough to pay their bills on time, or if they've been arrested, and other insights that may be important. Since you're letting a stranger into your parent's home, you might want to invest in some background information to be safe. You might want to collect an application fee from your most probable applicants to apply toward your search.

Once you and your parent have found the right person, write up a month-to-month rental agreement to spell out all the responsibilities of being a roommate. For instance, duties might include taking out the trash, washing dirty dishes, and doing laundry. Enter all of your parent's expectations in writing so there's no chance for misunderstandings later. Then, you (if you're managing or brokering this agreement), your parent, and the potential roommate should sign the rental agreement. There are plenty of sample rental agreements for your state that can be found online that meet the legal requirements of your state.

You may provide the light, power, and trash for free, but I caution against sharing an internet provider. It's important to keep your ISP to yourself to avoid hacking, and you never know what a roommate may be searching for online that could get you in trouble.

However nice they start out; roommates tend to be temporary. It can be challenging to find a match that lasts a long time. Petty grievances can fester and grow into major problems. If your parent isn't used to having other people around, they may experience difficulty adjusting to another person's habits—no matter how well they seemed to match initially. However, I knew a widow who made a lifetime friend by opening her home to an elderly man looking for a room. A little risk can sometimes reap big rewards.

 ## Reverse Mortgages

If your parent is short on cash and their home is their only major asset, a reverse mortgage may be an option, but be careful. The FBI and the U.S. Department of Housing and Urban Development Office of Inspector General (HUD-OIG) urge consumers, especially senior citizens, to be vigilant when seeking reverse mortgage products. These mortgages have created significant opportunities for fraud perpetrators.

They recommend a legitimate Home Equity Conversion Mortgages loan product insured by the Federal Housing Authority. It enables eligible homeowners to access the equity in their homes by providing funds without incurring a monthly payment.

With a reverse mortgage, your parent gets a loan in which the lender pays them part or all of their home's equity. The money they receive is usually tax-free, and they don't have to pay it back for as long as they live in their home. When they die, sell the house, or move out, their spouse or estate repays the loan. That often means selling the home to repay the loan. It doesn't mean that the loan company swoops in and reclaims the house.

There are three kinds of reverse mortgages:

- **Single-purpose reverse mortgages**—offered by state and local government agencies or nonprofits.

- **Proprietary reverse mortgages**—basically private loans.

- **Federally-insured reverse mortgages**—also known as Home Equity Conversion Mortgages (HECMs).

With a reverse mortgage, your parent (or their trust) keeps the title to their home. They get an advance on part of their home equity. When the last surviving borrower dies, sells the house, or no longer lives in the house as a principal residence, the loan has to be repaid. The money is usually is not taxable. It generally won't affect their Social Security or Medicare benefits, but contact an attorney to avoid surprises.

Here are some things to consider about reverse mortgages:

- **There are other fees and costs**. Reverse mortgage lenders often charge an origination fee, additional closing costs, and other fees during the life of the mortgage. Some also charge mortgage insurance premiums.

- **You owe more over time**. As your parent receives money through a reverse mortgage, interest is added to the balance they owe each month. The interest they owe grows as time marches on.

- **Interest rates may rise over time**. Some reverse mortgages—mostly HECMs—offer fixed rates. Still, most reverse mortgages have variable rates tied to a financial index that fluctuates.

- **Interest is not tax-deductible each year**. Interest on reverse mortgages is not deductible on income tax returns—until the loan is paid off.

- **Your parent is still responsible for other costs related to their home**. Property taxes, homeowner's insurance, utilities, fuel, maintenance, and other expenses must still be paid.

If your parent is a homebody and needs a little cash, a reverse mortgage may present an option. But encourage them to heed the advice from the FBI and the Federal Department of Housing and be vigilant in their search.

Live-in Care

Live-in care in exchange for room and board is another possibility. In this arrangement, your parent rents out extra space for less than the going rate for someone who agrees in a written contract to chores such as shopping, cooking, washing dishes, cleaning, yard work, and transportation.

The live-in roommate arrangement seems to work well with responsible college students looking for low-cost housing in exchange for assuming some limited responsibilities. I remember it appeared attractive when I was a poor college student. I stayed in an unfinished basement in an older woman's house and received reduced rent in exchange for yard work and shopping for her.

A roommate or live-in care arrangement is often a short-term solution to a long-term need. Roommates or live-in renters may not last beyond a few years. But good things can happen and your parent may just find the right person and establish a beautiful, long-lasting relationship.

National Organizations for Housing

Using the search term *"senior housing"* in your web browser will bring up hundreds of options promoting senior housing options near you. Below are a few websites that may help your search for senior housing.

- **National Shared Housing** (www.nationalsharedhousing.org) is a nonprofit foundation that helps seniors locate shared housing and list their homes for others. They have chapters in practically every city of every state.

- **Department of Housing and Urban Development**— Information for Senior Citizens (https://www.hud.gov/topics/information_for_senior_citizens/) this government site offers financial assistance resources, housing choice guides, information on federal housing programs for seniors, and much more.

- **Housing Help** (https://www.usa.gov/housing-help-audiences/) is a government website with tips on avoiding scams, finding affordable housing, and looking for the help you need for everything from disputes to home improvements.

Option 3: A Senior Apartment

If your parent is independent and comfortable living on their own but just wants to be closer to other people their age, consider a senior apartment. They are often located in large buildings in an urban setting and have many advantages. Your parent will be living with others in the same age range, so they're bound to make a friend or two. They're also fairly inexpensive and usually located near shopping malls, movies, dining and transportation. Some also provide outings, social activities, laundry services, and meals.

Moving your parent to a senior apartment may require adjustments, especially if your parent lives a rural life. It may take an adjustment for them to get used to apartment living in an urban environment.

You can find senior apartments near you listed on the web. Check the location first to make sure you like the neighborhood. Conduct a surveillance tour. Walk into the lobby unannounced. Is there a guard at the door to find out what you're doing there? Be candid and tell him you're checking the place out for your parent. Take the tour or take the elevator up yourself. Does it appear to be a warm, fresh-smelling place? Are there security cameras watching? Do the people living there appear happy and friendly? Can you imagine your parent interacting with them? Ask yourself if your parent would feel comfortable and safe there.

On your surveillance tour, take a walk through the neighborhood. Are the buildings well maintained? Are there bars over the windows of the homes? Do the neighbors appear friendly and helpful? You can use *Figure 4-1* to keep track of the senior apartments you visit and use it later to help evaluate your favorites. Use the numbers to rate (with the highest being the best.) Photocopy and fill out for each place.

Sample Evaluation Checklist for a Senior Apartment

Apartment name _____

Address _____

Price per month _____ Move-in cost _____

Location ① ② ③ ④ ⑤ _____

Lighting and smell ① ② ③ ④ ⑤ _____

Security ① ② ③ ④ ⑤ _____

Condition of elevator ① ② ③ ④ ⑤ _____

Current residents ① ② ③ ④ ⑤ _____

Available transportation ① ② ③ ④ ⑤ _____

Government assistance ① ② ③ ④ ⑤ _____

Length of waiting list ① ② ③ ④ ⑤ _____

Amenities included ① ② ③ ④ ⑤ _____

Overall impression ① ② ③ ④ ⑤ _____

Availability ① ② ③ ④ ⑤ _____

_____

Figure 4-1 *Sample Evaluation Checklist for a Senior Apartment*

How Much Does a Senior Apartment Cost?

A senior apartment can be government subsidized and cost as little as $200 to more than $3,500 per month, depending on location and type of housing.

To learn more about government subsidized housing in your area, visit:

- **Department of Housing and Urban Development** (www.hud.gov/)
- **Local Housing Solutions** (www.localhousingsolutions.org/)
- **Find Affordable Rental Housing** (www.usa.gov/finding-home)

Option 4: An Independent-Living Retirement Home

Retirement homes are usually apartment-type complexes with interior halls that are well-maintained and quiet. A resident is treated to two or three meals a day in a restaurant-style setting for a fixed monthly fee. Most feature exercise programs such as yoga, tai chi, golf, and weekly outings to plays or movies. Transportation is usually provided by a van owned by the complex. Some provide morning walks. Occasionally they'll even have their own golf courses. Most have beauty salons on site. They may even provide live music concerts several nights a month. A few have their own bars with featured happy hours, there may be built-in movie theaters, libraries, and chapels. Every holiday becomes the main event that shifts the social director into overdrive with new exciting programs that encourage socialization and fun.

These retirement homes can be like cruise ships on land. If your parent socializes well with others, they'll fit right in, as the opportunities abound. But if your parent is a loner, you may be paying for services they likely won't use. It's unlikely they'll morph into a social butterfly at this late stage of their life, although you could be surprised, as it does happen.

What the Rooms Are Like

Most of the rooms seem like small apartments, with kitchens and private baths. Moving from a private home to one of these tiny apartments can be a big adjustment. You may have to rent storage space for some of your parent's possessions if they insist on holding on to them. But the plethora of social opportunities offered in this type of retirement oasis can make the sacrifice worth the move. If your parent lacks friends and is lonely, these social havens provide everyday opportunities to meet and share activities with others. Your parent may be happy to rent out or sell their old home to help make the rental payments at one of these communities.

How Much Does an Independent Living Retirement Apartment Cost?

Costs vary with location, type of programs available, and the amount of experience of the staff. Figure on somewhere from $1,500 to $5,500 per month depending on location and amenities offered. But keep in mind that this cost covers nearly everything—even transportation to medical appointments. Medical and dental care, hair care, and beauty treatments usually aren't covered in the monthly fee. Some "exclusive" apartments may require large down payments to keep out the "riff raff" and ensure their exclusivity.

How to Find a Good Independent Living Community

Search the Internet for "*independent living near me*" or type in the city your parent lives in. All types of sites will pop up advertising places with images of happy older people enjoying themselves in brightly lit rooms. Some sites will even help you filter your results based on comments and price. Take notes and plan to visit a few of them for a bit of recon trip. Go visit a few of these homes completely unannounced. Linger in the lobby and use your nose as a guide. Does it smell fresh? Or does it smell stale and musty? Is there fresh coffee and newspapers for residents? Do the people working there seem happy?

Look at the residents. Ask yourself, "Are they happy to be living here?" Do they smile at you when you smile at them, or do they stare straight ahead? Watch how the residents interact with staff. Do they interact in a friendly way, or is it suspicious and guarded? The staff of a retirement home can make or break the social environment. If they seem to relate well and professionally with the residents, chances are you've found a good place.

The decision really comes down to whether you feel comfortable leaving your parent in their hands. You can use *Figure 4-2* to help you evaluate and keep track of your impressions of independent-living retirement homes. You could also take photos on your cell phone to help jog your memory later.

Evaluation Checklist
for an Independent Living Retirement Home

Name of facility _____

Address _____

Price per month _____ Phone _____

Location of facility ① ② ③ ④ ⑤_____

Lighting and cleanliness ① ② ③ ④ ⑤_____

Security ① ② ③ ④ ⑤_____

Smell ① ② ③ ④ ⑤_____

Residents ① ② ③ ④ ⑤_____

Transportation provided ① ② ③ ④ ⑤_____

Social calendar ① ② ③ ④ ⑤_____

Staff ① ② ③ ④ ⑤_____

Meals ① ② ③ ④ ⑤_____

Available rooms ① ② ③ ④ ⑤_____

Hair salon ① ② ③ ④ ⑤ _____

Overall impression ① ② ③ ④ ⑤ _____

Assisted living provided? _____

Special dietary needs provided? _____

Parking space provided? _____

Other impressions: _____

_____

_____

Figure 4-2 *Evaluation Checklist for an Independent Living Retirement Home*

Once you've picked a few favorites by scouting ahead on a solo reconnaissance tour, get one of your family members to come along with you and your parent to do final evaluations.

Compare prices, as they can vary widely. To save, consider a neighboring community. As in the game of Monopoly, Boardwalk and Park Place may be the coveted areas for a retirement home, but Atlantic or even Vermont Avenue may offer nearly the same for much less.

Most of these independent-living retirement homes are built like fortresses with a courtyard and a pool in the middle. Your parent will probably be more impressed by the services and the people inside, rather than the actual physical location—especially if the complex offers transportation. Chances are, they'll become spoiled and use their car less as time goes on.

Surprises on the Hunt

In hunting for an independent living retirement home for Mom, I found five totally different types.

1. A swank new-age facility managed by aging hippies with long flowing hair. The maintenance workers looked like members of a motorcycle group. Incense was burning in the lobby. Soothing sitar music played in the background. The place was a bargain, but I didn't want Mom living there. It felt like a front for a drug operation.

2. An aging high-rise apartment building that reeked of mold and urine. I couldn't find the social director and the residents appeared like they were stuck in a place that time had forgotten. No one could give me a tour without an appointment. They were just too busy.

3. A family-managed community that appeared well-maintained. However, the staff permitted older, "disabled" children to stay with the residents. Several of these children were in their 30s and having a beer bust near the community pool.

4. A religious-based retirement home that seemed to have high moral standards and strict rules but appeared old and smelled musty.

5. A well-run facility staffed by professionals where guests seem happy. It smelled fresh without the aid of plug-ins. Photos of their last social function were on display. The pool was well maintained, and residents were frolicking in it.

Looking back at my own mom, I'm glad that she had the opportunity to stay in one of these retirement communities before moving on to a board and care home. Knowing what I know now, I wish we had applied pressure on her to move sooner than we did. At least we were able to help her out of a solitary existence and into a whirlwind of socialization, if only for a few years.

Downsides of an Independent Living Retirement Home

If your parent lives alone at home, you may have to rent storage space for their belongings as they move to their small independent living apartment. Later, they may realize they don't need all that stuff anymore, and you can arrange a yard sale to help pay for their needs.

If your parent was used to rural life, they'll have to adjust to the noises of apartment living, such as the sound of toilets flushing. The natural sounds of birds may be replaced by the perpetual sound of their neighbor's TV. Even the perks will require some adjustment. Dinner arriving in the dining room every night is a plus, but not if their appetite is on a different timetable.

Try to look at each facility as a place your parent will stay for some time. Moving to a new home is difficult for anyone. It doesn't become easier as you grow older.

 ## Helping with the Adjustment of Moving

Studies have consistently shown that moving can be as stressful as divorce or the death of a loved one. Where your parent lives isn't just their nest, it's a canvas that their memories have been painted on. These memories are part of them, and they include you. This attachment can be profound, playing a pivotal role in how they see themselves. Any interference with this attachment can cause stress. Add this disruption to the other factors that accompany a move—the stress of looking for a new place, packing, deciding what to put in storage, and your parent can be easily overwhelmed.

You can help them by being there to box their belongings and offering them support. Remind them of the other places they've moved from in the past. Help them walk around their old house to take a last look before leaving. Perhaps you have a memory to share with them (as this can also be stressful for you). Make a collage of old photos or memorabilia they can bring to their new home. Let them say goodbye, and don't rush them. Let them mourn moving from their old place, and then turn their attention forward.

Help your parent to look forward to the move. Remind them how their life will start new and refreshed in an exciting place with new friends to meet. Help them set up new patterns and develop familiarity with their new home. Bring photos and memory-evoking items. Remind them that you'll come to visit them often.

Can Your Parent Afford an Independent Living Retirement Home?

The most significant problem with housing is usually cost. If the cost is manageable, will the perks be worth the hassle of the move? Will they really fit in with the crowd there? Most of all, can they afford it? To find out, add up all their monthly sources of income and expenses:

Monthly Income and Expenses Worksheet

Unless your parent has hit the lottery, they may have limited sources of income. Sit down with them and help them figure out how much monthly income is coming in.

Possible Income Sources:

- Pension _____
- Social security _____
- Rental income _____
- Annuities _____

- Bonds _____
- Stocks _____
- Other _____
- Other _____

Total _____

Will they still need a drink of that expensive whiskey every evening? How about playing the lotto or donating to charity? There will always be expenses that you don't need to know about. This list is just to help you get a preliminary estimate of their monthly expenses.

Possible Monthly Expenses:

- Retirement facility _____

- Utilities _____

- Phone (cell/landline) _____

- Internet/cable (if not provided)
  _____

- Storage _____

- Snacks/food away from facility
  _____

- Grooming _____

- Car payment/insurance _____

- Doctor visits _____

- Supplemental medical
  insurance _____

- Prescriptions _____

- Pet supplies _____

- Dependent expenses _____

- Miscellaneous expenses
  _____

- Other _____

- Other _____

Total _____

Figure 4-3 *Monthly Income and Expenses Worksheet*

You may have to help your parent liquidate some of these assets to provide them with a better way of life. It's also good for you to know what resources your parent has if you have to take charge of them someday. Completing this form will also help you become aware of debts your parent may have incurred.

Most seniors have assets set aside somewhere. Your job here is to help them improve their lifestyle, using their assets. Use the Personal Financial Worksheet shown in *Figure 4-4* to help tabulate all assets, including hidden ones they may have forgotten about. You can help them accumulate a record of their financial institutions and account numbers.

Personal Financial Worksheet

Asset	Possible Value (low estimate)
Home or other real property	_____
Home or other real property	_____
Home or other real property	_____
Home or other real property	_____
Car(s)	_____
Appliances	_____
Jewelry	_____
Collectibles	_____
Coins	_____
Tools	_____
Other	_____

Bank Accounts
(including checking, savings, money market, and Certificates of Deposits)

Bank _____

Acct no. _____ Current amount _____

Bank _____

Acct no. _____ Current amount _____

Bank _____

Acct no. _____ Current amount _____

Other Investments

(stocks, bonds, savings bonds, treasury notes, mutual funds, etc.)

Type   **Value**

_____   _____

_____   _____

_____   _____

_____   _____

Tax-deferred Accounts

(limited partnerships, annuities, IRA's, profit-sharing plans, pensions, etc.)

Type   **Value**

_____   _____

_____   _____

_____   _____

_____   _____

Parent's Debts

(mortgage, auto loans, credit card, and all other personal debts)

Type   **Value**

_____   _____

_____   _____

_____   _____

_____   _____

Figure 4-4 *Personal Financial Worksheet*

Assisted Living in an Independent Living Retirement Home

Some independent retirement homes have a wing or particular building identified as the assisted living section. This section adds one more level of care available to residents should they need it. It also means that a full-time nurse is usually on the grounds should an accident occur, and a quick medical assessment is needed. Perhaps your parent is staying in the *independent* living section of a retirement home and just needs a little extra help. An aide from the *assisted* living section can arrive to dispense medications or help with bathing or showering. This usually involves an extra monthly fee, but it's still considerably cheaper than moving your parent to a full-blown nursing home where they're paying for amenities they may not need at this time.

Option 5: Three-Part Care Facility

Because moving can be so stressful, some opt for the whole life option of a three-part care facility. Three levels of care include:

1. **Independent Living:** In this section, the residents come and go as they choose. There are social activities, excursions, and plenty of socialization.

2. **Assisted Living:** As they need more care, they move into an assisted living wing. The assisted living wing may be like a mini-nursing home. It's usually staffed with full-time nurses.

3. **Locked 24-hour Care:** Finally, there is a locked wing of the facility. This wing provides the third level of care, 24 hours a day, for demented and Alzheimer's patients unable to look after themselves.

Occasionally, a three-part care facility will have a full-scale nursing home, a hospice, and a funeral home. A basic one-stop-shop, this is the true "last roundup."

These facilities can be huge. Besides the number of social activities they offer, they usually have such a wide assortment of people that your parent is bound to meet someone like themselves. Having a full-time nursing staff on duty is an added plus, especially when something goes wrong in the middle of the night.

The Downside of a Three-Part Care Facility

The downside of a three-part facility is that they are so large they may lose the personal touch. Nurses may be rotated before they can get to know their patients. I've known people who have taken their parent out of a large institutional setting and into a smaller residential care facility—which we'll get to next. It really depends on how your parent feels about it, as they're the ones living there. They might enjoy seeing their friends from the early days at the Independent Living wing joining them a few years later in the Assisted Living section.

How Much Does a Three-Part Facility Cost?

Three-part care facilities usually start out at the same level as retirement homes. The price goes up with the level of care needed as add-ons. The overhead of these places is high, with doctors and nurses on staff. The costs are then passed on to the residents. They are often run by corporations that must increase their profit margins.

Feel free to check out a few of these medical metropolises for your own education. Go unannounced on a Saturday for a solo fact-finding visit. They're usually happy to take you on tour. Check with your nose as well as your eyes. Do you smell excrement or urine? Or do you smell bleach and disinfectant? Ask yourself the regular questions—does the staff have the ability to easily communicate with your parent? Do they willingly answer your questions? Do the residents appear happy? Would you feel comfortable leaving your parent there? If you're satisfied with what you see, make an appointment to bring your parent back along with your family for an official tour.

Option 6: A Board and Care Home

Not everyone is familiar with board and care homes. In some states, they're referred to as adult foster care homes. These residential facilities provide 24-hour assisted-living care for your parent with various outings and social activities. They're usually unmarked and located in residential neighborhoods. Up to eight older people may live in a family-type setting where the manager also stays. Meals are provided, as is transportation to the doctor's office, hairdresser, and sometimes movies and plays. Some provide transportation to the local senior center each day. Others even offer ocean or lake cruises.

Trained employees, referred to as caregivers, assist residents with daily needs. These aren't skilled nurses, but they're there to provide for your parent's basic needs. At least one staff member must be CPR certified and on the premises 24 hours. Any personnel who provide care to the residents must have first-aid certification. All personnel and some volunteers must have a Criminal Record Clearance before employment approval. Each caregiver has a shift of time when they're on duty. They sometimes sleep nearby in case they're needed during the night.

In a decent board and care home, a family atmosphere prevails. Meals are often served at a table in the dining room. Since a staff member is often cooking and serving meals to residents, they can quickly notice any changes in appetite that may indicate health issues.

Board and care facilities are usually licensed by the state, and though each state has its own guidelines, they all work to protect the clients living in these homes. A board and care home is required to keep voluminous files on its residents so that if anything goes wrong—they have records. The state may conduct surprise periodic inspections to ensure licensing requirements are being met.

Board and care homes often group the people living in each home by the amount of care they require. This works to everyone's advantage. Your parent will make friends with other residents needing the same type of care and hopefully become a member of the "family." As your parent ages and requires more care, they can move to another facility, joining others who also need increased care.

HELPING YOUR AGING PARENT

Board and care homes are operated by private citizens who are individual entrepreneurs. Since these are small-time operations, the level of care provided can range dramatically. Unlike the large institutional care facilities, there is no board of directors, no marketing staff or social director. It's usually one chief wearing many hats who has a whole lot of employees working under them. Some states require the administrator to complete a certification course. The administrator may have to complete 40 hours of continuing education units every two years, depending on your state's licensing requirements.

A good board and care can provide personalized attention. The caregivers usually have fewer people to look after, so they get to know each person as an individual. If there are changes in your parent's behavior or health, the caregiver may notice it before you do and call you to request permission to take your parent to the doctor.

Another thing about an excellent residential board and care facility is that usually, it has operated in the community for years. Over those years, it has developed a support network of geriatric doctors, nurses, and medical suppliers. The board and care home can recommend a wide range of top-notch geriatric health care providers through this support network. These recommendations may include doctors, nurses, lawyers, notary publics, dentists, and even hairdressers. This can be a real Godsend if your parent suddenly needs a dentist, doctor, or nurse. Often, the residential board and care staff will take your parent to the medical appointments or even the hospital and be there with them through the whole procedure if you can't. Some board and care facilities even provide hospice care.

If you want to avoid an expensive nursing home for a while, consider a residential board and care home. While they may not provide 24-hour "nursing" care, they usually come close and cost less. In a residential board and care facility, your parent will usually get intensive care at a considerably lower cost than what they'd pay in a larger assisted living facility. One of the most efficient things about a board and care residential facility is that the director is usually available to answer questions. As your parent gets older and has more ailments, you're probably going to have many more questions. It's generally easier to get answers in a smaller facility.

How Much Does a Board and Care Facility Cost?

Residential board and care facilities usually start out at the same level as retirement homes—at this time, around $3,500 to $6,500 per month, depending on location and level of care required.

How to Find a Good Board and Care Facility

Residential board and care homes often rely on reputation and word-of-mouth advertising. Social services or the senior center in your community may list phone numbers of board and care facilities. You can usually find out about board and care homes through social workers or geriatric counselors. Sometimes hospitals or geriatric clinics will refer you. There are private rooms and shared room setups. Some residential care facilities are so popular that there are waiting lists to get in. If you're considering one for your parent, you should start to visit a few.

The first action to take when evaluating a residential board and care is to call the director and set up an appointment for a meeting. A residential care director may be responsible for more than one board and care facility. The director will ask you about your parent's specific medical needs and the type of care they'll need. Then, they can match your parent with a home that has a room available.

As you walk in the front door, ask yourself if it feels like a happy place? Would you feel comfortable coming there to visit your parent at any time of day? Do the residents seem happy? Does the staff appear to interact well with them? Are they getting enough exercise, or are they stuck like zombies in front of the TV all day? Is there an outdoor patio or garden for sitting or recreation?

While having everyone stuck in front of a TV may make it easy for the caregivers, it isn't too healthy for the residents. Mom stayed at one of these for a while. My sister and I had to come on weekends to get Mom out and away from the TV and give her a little physical exercise.

Take a look at the social calendar for the facility. It should be posted in clear sight on a wall. Are there activities your parent would enjoy? Do they take the residents out to lunch occasionally, to the movies, to the hairdresser, or outings?

Also, check the meals provided. Are they receiving lots of green vegetables and fiber? As the body ages and gets less exercise, regularity can become a problem. Does the diet contain lots of starchy foods with little fiber? Or does it provide good nutrition that features salads and bran? You don't want your parent to wind up with a blocked colon, a fairly common problem among older people that can be life-threatening. Ask the caregivers if they're willing to serve salads and bran daily. If they give you a blank stare, move on.

Find out if cranberry juice is regularly on the menu. Why? Older people, especially older women, are susceptible to urinary tract infections. These infections can go undiagnosed for months and can affect the balance of electrolytes in the body. This can lead to bizarre symptoms that may be difficult to diagnose. Cranberry juice (*not* cranberry "drink") has been shown to help prevent or reduce the severity of urinary tract infections. Hopefully, the care facility already knows this. A board and care facility should be flexible enough to add bran or cranberry juice to your parent's diet if you ask for it. Ask questions. You have a right to know, and your parent's health should be important to any facility.

Get several references from families whose parents have stayed in the facility. While you're touring—especially on the weekend—you may even meet a few families at the facility. Take them aside and ask them how long their parent has been there. Ask them how they feel about leaving their parent there. Check out at least three board and care facilities before settling on one. You can use *Figure 4-5* to help you evaluate them. Make copies and keep track of your impressions at various locations. Take photos with your phone to jog your memory when comparing later.

Evaluation Checklist for a Residential Board and Care Facility

Name of facility _____

Address _____

Price per month _____ Phone _____

Location of facility ① ② ③ ④ ⑤_____

Lighting and cleanliness ① ② ③ ④ ⑤_____

Caregivers ① ② ③ ④ ⑤_____

Smell ① ② ③ ④ ⑤_____

Dining room ① ② ③ ④ ⑤_____

Residents ① ② ③ ④ ⑤_____

Transportation ① ② ③ ④ ⑤_____

Entertainment/activities ① ② ③ ④ ⑤_____

Social calendar ① ② ③ ④ ⑤_____

Meals/diet ① ② ③ ④ ⑤_____

Available rooms ① ② ③ ④ ⑤_____

Hair salon/beauty treatments ① ② ③ ④ ⑤_____

Exercise ① ② ③ ④ ⑤_____

Pertinent Questions

Special assistance provided?   ☐ yes   ☐ no

Special dietary needs?   ☐ yes   ☐ no

Caregivers speak your parent's language?   ☐ yes   ☐ no

Can you examine the state licensing reports for the home?   ☐ yes   ☐ no

Are there costs beyond basic care?   ☐ yes   ☐ no

Does the facility offer hospice care?   ☐ yes   ☐ no

Can your parent keep their own physician?   ☐ yes   ☐ no

Can your parent use their own furniture & TV?   ☐ yes   ☐ no

Can your parent keep their own phone?   ☐ yes   ☐ no

Can your parent have a pet?   ☐ yes   ☐ no

Does the home provide overnight staffing?   ☐ yes   ☐ no

Can family members visit at any time?   ☐ yes   ☐ no

Shared or private room? _____

_____

Figure 4-5 *Evaluation Checklist for a Residential Board and Care Facility*

Living with Your Housing Decision

Finding a place for your parent to stay can be an ongoing challenge. But finding a residence you and your parent are comfortable with is one of the most important decisions you can make. At first, this decision will probably heavily involve your parent. Later, if their ability to make decisions diminishes, it will be primarily your own effort with the help of your family. Hopefully, some of the information included in this chapter will be useful and help you prevent some of the mistakes that my sister and I made.

When you take responsibility for the location of your parent's new home, doubts will inevitably creep in about your decision—no matter how much you may have researched the new venue. Making permanent choices that affect the lives of others is hard.

You may not find a place that fulfills your parent's wish list. As a popular song from the Rolling Stones goes, "You can't always get what you want. But if you try some times, you get what you need."

Hospitals today are filled will well-meaning but over-worked staff that can make mistakes.

Chapter 5
SURVIVING THE HOSPITAL

A call for an emergency trip to the hospital is never a good omen, except maybe for the birth of a new baby. When a call from the hospital concerns your aging parent, it never seems to arrive at a convenient time.

My journey to the hospital began with a call from the board and care home where Mom was staying. They informed me that she hadn't been eating well and now she was throwing up something with a foul odor. I met the caregiver in the same busy hospital emergency room in which my dad had died six years earlier. Everything seemed disorganized when I arrived. Mom looked tired but thankful that I was finally there. Amid the noise and confusion around us, we got her admitted through the emergency entrance, which took about four hours.

Within a day, they'd run a battery of tests, sticking tubes in Mom's every orifice. Confronted with the results, we had to make a quick decision. Her DNR prohibited resuscitation, but she was running a fever and growing weaker every hour. She needed an operation to stay alive.

If she did have the operation, machines might be used to keep her alive for a while. Surviving meant she would spend the rest of her life with a colostomy bag. That would be a difficult challenge for my mom. There was no clear-cut answer. We decided to operate and try and prolong her life.

What I learned was that an elderly person in the hospital needs an alert advocate. While Mom was in the hospital, she was given a drug that she was allergic to (even though her allergy to the drug was written in her records when she was admitted). She suffered a heart attack and had a catheter improperly inserted in her that extended her bladder, causing an infection that hindered her healing process. She also developed bedsores.

What I found out during that time would forever change how I view hospitals. I always assumed that these shelters of care were safe, quiet places—refuges where a highly trained and caring staff looked after you. Unfortunately, overworked staff can and sometimes do make mistakes. With you as a cautious advocate, your parent may be spared a similar experience. I'm sharing my regrets here for your benefit.

Don't Panic

As a child of an aging parent, nothing can prepare you for the phone call that your parent has been rushed to the hospital and that you need to get there right away. Your mind is racing a hundred miles an hour and in a thousand different directions.

Keeping your emotional and mental state in control is key. Calm down. Collect your emotions, and let your rational side take the lead. Collect your parent's Power of Attorney for Health Care, the Drug Allergy Notice (included in this chapter), and the Prescription Drug List in Chapter 2. Muster up your courage, and head out to the hospital. Hospitals are stressful places to visit. There's nothing much worse than having someone you love there.

Not to scare you but consumer advocate Ralph Nader determined that 300,000 to 600,000 people die every year because of medical incompetence. That would be like having casualties from 6 to 12 Vietnam Wars every year in our own country. Yet, this is how many people die every year from doctor and hospital mistakes. It's important to not be complacent while your parent is in the hospital. Probably the worst thing you can do is not become involved at all. Sometimes, when a loved one is in the hospital, it becomes easy to detach yourself from the emotions and pain of the situation. Try not to let that happen to you because if a situation comes up, and you could have prevented or stopped it, it will be you who suffers the guilt of knowing that later.

 ## What is Medicare?

Medicare is a federal program that helps older or disabled people pay their medical bills. It's an entitlement program available to both the rich and the poor. Most U.S. citizens or residents of the United States for five years who are over 65 can qualify for enrollment. Those who aren't U.S. citizens or haven't paid into Medicare may enroll and make monthly payments to receive coverage. Medicare usually pays for hospitalization and nursing home care for up to 60 consecutive days. Medicare comes in two parts:

- Part A is for hospital insurance and covers most of the costs of a stay in a hospital and some follow-up costs after a stay in the hospital. To get Medicare to cover hospital care, you must be admitted by a doctor or the emergency room.

- Part B is medical insurance that pays for some doctor and outpatient medical care. It usually pays for doctor expenses, exams, tests, ambulance rides to the hospital or nursing home, X-rays, hospital beds, wheelchairs, and the paraphernalia supplied by hospitals. It also offers some occupational therapy and counseling by psychologists and social workers. Your parent is billed for the rest unless they have supplementary insurance.

Medicare parts A and B don't pay all costs. You should make sure your parent has supplemental insurance to pay expenses not covered by Medicare. Otherwise, your parent will have to pay the difference.

Medicare Advantage plans offer a hybrid package that provides health care and Medicare part D prescription care and vision, dental, and hearing care.

Getting Your Parent Admitted to the Hospital

Sometimes how your parent is admitted to the hospital determines if Medicare pays the hospital costs or not. If you have control over the admission process, ask your parent's doctor to have them admitted with a written order. Ask the doctor's office to call in the admission order ahead of their arrival. If you don't have time for this, and the problem is acute, you'll have to admit them from the emergency room.

If your parent is unable to sign themselves, they'll need your help to fill out the admission forms. Make sure that everything is listed correctly and nothing important is omitted. You may have to provide some form of legal identification for both your parent and yourself, so make sure you have both you and your parent's driver's license on hand, as well as their Medicare number, and proof of any supplemental insurance. Do not sign any document accepting responsibility for payment of your parent's treatment, unless you are prepared to pay it.

Be sure to list any allergies and possible reactions to the allergic substance. Complement the list with the Prescription Drug List from Chapter 2. Be sure to include aspirin, Tylenol, and any substance for energizing or relaxing. Ensure the hospital knows what drugs your parent is allergic to (*Figure 5-1*) and every pre-existing medical condition your parent may have.

It's not taboo to come right out and ask if your parent's insurance or Medicare will pay for the entire hospital stay. Have available the name(s) of the primary care physician and the specialists that treat your parent. List all of your parent's medical conditions and all surgeries (all means all, not just the most recent—including elective plastic surgery).

If you haven't yet taken your parent to the hospital, but know in advance that a hospital stay is looming, try and fill out the admittance papers ahead of time. Some hospitals post them online for you to download and fill out. You'll spare your parent the hardship of filling out volumes of forms at admission. Helping your parent and being there to take charge during the hospital admission is one of the best things you can do for them, and it's probably what they would do for you.

What Is an Adverse Event?

An "adverse event" is when something happens that causes harm to a patient due to medical care. It's what you want to try and avoid by being proactive in your parent's care.

Once in the hospital, your parent will be involved in many procedures and tests. You'll be on the sidelines, offering encouragement and watching over them. Many things can go wrong in a hospital, and many of these things will be out of your control. On the other hand, there are some things you can do to take control of your parent's hospital stay, even if you can only come to see your parent during visiting hours.

Studies estimate that one million patients nationwide are injured by errors during hospital treatment each year. According to a 2016 study by Johns Hopkins, these errors result in over 250,000 deaths each year, making it one of the leading causes of death in the U.S. New laws were passed in 2008 requiring hospitals to report their "adverse events" to the Office of the Inspector General.

According to the Office of the Inspector General, more than one in four Medicare beneficiaries experience some degree of harm while hospitalized. The chance of a mistake increases with the length of stay in the hospital. Most of the mistakes occur during monitoring and daily care. Below, I've listed a few things you can do and what to watch out for.

Find What's Going On

If your parent has already been admitted and you're just arriving at the hospital, ask to talk to a head nurse. Staff is limited and often overworked.

The head nurse may be able to tell you what's going on. Be prepared to wait if you have to. Give the nurse your Power of Attorney for Health Care discussed in Chapter 3, and let them make a copy for their files. Present them with a list of medications your parent is taking from Chapter 2 and those your parent is allergic to (*Figure 5-1*).

Sometimes the head nurse will only tell you so much about your parent's prognosis, and then you'll have to wait for the doctor. If both seem purposely vague or secretive, it may be because there's more to the problem than they want to get into. If they're not answering your questions, ask for a second opinion. A good doctor should welcome a second opinion on their diagnosis. You now have to be your parent's advocate.

Start with a calm demeanor. You have a right to answers. If necessary, bring in reinforcements—a platoon of concerned relatives politely yet forcefully demanding straight answers makes a difference. Use your phone. Google the medicine or treatment they recommend. Search for side effects and adverse reactions. Use what you discover to ask more questions if necessary.

Read up on Your Parent's Diagnosed Situation

Go to the hospital's website and access your parent's doctor's notes on their condition. Empower yourself with knowledge. Google your parent's ailment and search for medical research on the ailment or condition. Access Google Scholar. Then, when the doctor asks you to make a decision on your parent's health care, your answer will probably be based on knowledge from this search and others like it in the days to follow. You'll also be prepared to ask the doctor some questions of your own.

Nurses Are People Too

Try to get to know the nurses on a personal level. They have a difficult job caring for many patients while working long, hard hours. They're more "hands-on" and involved in patient care than physicians, so they may detect a change in medical status before anyone else. They'll be the first to notice if your parent has an unusual reaction to some new drug that the doctor recommended. They'll usually be the first to catch sight of bedsores.

You'll want to feel that the nurses are on your side, fighting against any unknown infection or surprise condition that can happen to your parent during their hospital stay. Chances are, you'll meet a new nurse every time you come in to see your parent. Be friendly and make it your job to try and get to know all the nurses that take care of your parent. They're hard at work in the trenches, so show them respect. Be patient if they're busy and can't get to you or your parent right away. Remember, they have other patients to attend to. Even though it may be difficult, try and see the world through their eyes.

Nurses are very knowledgeable about medicines. Ask them all the questions you need to. They usually won't feel that you're bothering them. In fact, they may feel flattered that you asked them. Sometimes it's a way you can get to know them. I ran all the new prescriptions by the nurses.

"That one produces side effects," the red-haired nurse whispered. "I suggest you try this one." She scratched down the name on a sheet of paper. "But you didn't hear it from me."

Sure enough, I checked online, and there were some nasty side effects listed for the drug the doctor had ordered. I went back to him and got a new prescription. I was happy I'd asked the nurse. She taught me a lot.

Lend a Hand

Nurses generally appreciate any help you give them. If your parent needs their mouth swabbed out, ask them if you can do it. If the room needs a little tidying, go ahead and clean. If your parent needs some help with feeding, ask if you can help. There will probably be some things that the nurses won't want you helping with, but you'll always win points for asking.

Speaking of brownie points, it probably won't hurt to bring in some cookies or a fruit basket for the nursing staff to show them your appreciation. Especially if the cookies are homemade or the fruit is from your own backyard. Try to make it a point to place a little basket of goodies at the nurses' station with every visit. Let them know you appreciate them. Many people take them for granted. The kindness you show here may be extended to your parent.

Have the Nurse Check the Catheter

When you visit your parent, if a nurse is there, ask them nicely to check the catheter. A catheter is used to help a hospital patient urinate without getting up out of bed. As a visitor, you'll see it as a tube coming from a mystery spot under the sheets and going into a bag filled with yellow liquid. At times the catheter can be improperly inserted or become dislodged.

This, in turn, can cause an infection or an extended bladder and a lot of pain. And sometimes, no one will have the presence of mind to check the catheter insertion. It should be checked between four to seven times a day. While you're visiting, it doesn't hurt to ask the nurse to check if it's properly inserted, especially if your parent is complaining about it. This is one of the most common infection points in older female hospital patients. Yet, we must rely on the nurses to check it. An infection here can sap your parent's strength and delay recovery. It doesn't hurt or cost anything to ask the nurse to check. Stand by and make sure she does it while you're there.

 ## The Medical Chart

The medical chart traditionally placed at the foot of a patient's bed was once the Rosetta Stone for posting progress on patients for hundreds of years. It contained a snapshot of their vitals and provided insight into their progress for any passing doctor or nurse. As privacy concerns became an issue, the charts were moved to computer records.

Starting April 2021, the U.S. Government required health organizations to make medical records available to patients electronically. Patients are now able to read their doctor's notes online. Doctor's notes include consultations, imaging and lab findings, medical history, exam findings, and more.

Preventing a Drug Allergy Reaction

Allergic reactions to hospital-administered drugs can be life-threatening. It happened to my mom when she was prescribed a medicine she was allergic to. We were summoned to the hospital as she was fading fast. No one had a clue what was happening until the nurse described what had happened. "She had a slight urinary infection, so we added sulfa to her IV."

My sister and I shot up straight. "Did it occur to you that she's allergic to sulfa, and it's listed in her records?"

"No," the nurse turned away. "Let me alert the doctor."

By copying, filling, and posting the Drug Allergy Notice on the wall next to your parent's bed, you'll be doing your best to prevent the hospital from administering a drug or item that your parent may be allergic to. The information may be in the files, but not every staff member reads every notation and remembers the contents. Post at eye-level to raise the odds that the nurse on duty will read it. Some hospitals have whiteboards with patient information, but an extra note won't hurt.

Drug Allergy Notice

The patient _____ is allergic to the following types of drugs:

- _____
- _____
- _____
- _____

- _____
- _____
- _____
- _____

Therefore, I request that you do not administer them.

They are also allergic to the following items:

_____

_____

_____

_____

Signed _____ Date _____

Relationship to patient _____

Figure 5-1 *Drug Allergy Notice*

How to Help Prevent Bedsores

If your parent remains in a hospital bed for over a week, certain parts of their body will bear all the pressure of their weight. Typically, these are elbows, heels, and buttocks. Pressure ulcers, better known as bedsores, can develop and even become infected. Sometimes they even appear on the boney areas of the upper back and the back of the head—where there's friction between your parent's body and the bed. All that friction creates stress and inflammation. Bedsores are the scourge of hospitals. Once they develop, they're tough to heal, especially if they ulcerate. Pressure ulcers weaken the immune system and make your parent more susceptible to other ailments.

If your parent develops bedsores, they can only be released from the hospital to an expensive nursing home where licensed nurses can care for them until the sores heal. It's in everyone's best interest to prevent bedsores from forming, and you can help.

Most hospitals require nurses to move a patient from side to side periodically, so the weight of their body shifts and isn't supported by the same pressure points. Some hospitals offer an inflatable bed or a motorized one that tilts back and forth like a boat rocking in slow motion to prevent a patient's weight from being supported on the same spot. You can request one of these beds to be ordered and delivered to the hospital.

In addition, every time you visit your parent in the hospital, check the heels of their feet. Are they soft and smooth? Or are they becoming red and callused on the heel area? If they are, or you notice a spot forming that feels warmer than the surrounding skin, ask a nurse what can be done. Upon request, many will provide sheepskin booties that wrap around the heel of the foot to prevent constant grinding of the heel against the sheets of the bed. Every time you return to the hospital, check to make sure the booties are still on and haven't worked themselves off.

Check your parent's elbows. Gently lift them up and look for any red spots. Have the nurse help you check the buttocks. Usually, if your parent is lying on their back most of the time, their weight will be supported by their buttocks. Bedsores are the hardest to see there and, therefore, most likely to fester. Don't be shy about asking a nurse to help. When the staff sees that you're being proactive in your parent's healthcare, they're often motivated to pay closer attention. Besides, this helpful activity also gives you a job every time you visit and takes the pressure off trying to make everyone laugh and cheer up.

The goal of your visits to your parent in the hospital should be to offer support, sympathy, and encouragement. Remind them that this is just a temporary stay and try and get them to enjoy it. Remind them how great the Jello tastes.

Bring them in a puzzle book. Make up silly nicknames for the doctors and nurses. Don't stand there looking sad. Your parent may hide their own feelings because they're worried about you. Get to work and massage their feet and elbows to avoid bedsores.

Lanolin or aloe ointment can be applied to your parent's heels and elbows. Work it in well. Try not to massage it directly into the red areas— just work at it from the sides. If you rub directly into a red spot, it will only increase the friction. By sticking to a massage regimen, you can reverse the formation of bedsores and keep them from becoming open wounds. Your parent may even appreciate the attention, which can offer you some control in what is often an uncontrollable situation.

How to Handle Privacy Issues

Hospitals can feel invasive, and personal care can be embarrassing—especially if your parent is sharing a room with someone who has a large family. In those times, your parent may wish for privacy during certain checks or procedures. If you or your parent is concerned about the lack of privacy in the hospital, post a large note like the one shown in *Figure 5-2*, asking all attendants to pull the curtain for privacy before giving an enema, inspection, or washing. Post this notice at eye level in the room, near your parent's bed, next to the drug allergy notice.

Personal Privacy Notice

The patient _____ would appreciate a certain

amount of personal privacy and would like to request that the curtain be

drawn when;

- Giving enemas
- Any physical exam
- Bathing or cleaning
- Using the bedpan

- Other _____
  _____
- Other _____
  _____

Signed _____ Date _____

Relationship to patient _____

Figure 5-2 *Personal Privacy Notice*

Surviving an Operation

If your parent needs an operation, here are a few things you can do to try
to make sure they receive the best care:

- Make sure all lab tests were completed and checked over by the attending doctor before the date scheduled for surgery. Talk to the doctor. He needs to know you care deeply about your parent and the outcome of the operation.

- Consult with the surgeon and anesthesiologist before the surgery. Find out exactly what they're planning to do. Ask them if the surgery is really necessary. How many times have they done this operation? What are the odds for a complete recovery? Get a clear understanding of the procedure, what it entails, and the risks involved.

- Ask about possible complications. Some people suffer post-operation blood clots, delirium, confusion, or other problems. Try and get a straight answer. You have a right to know.

- What happens next? Will your parent have to go to a nursing home? For how long? Will Medicare pay for it? How can you participate in the recovery process? How long should recovery take? What drugs will your parent take, and for how long? What are the side effects?

If you don't feel the surgery is necessary, don't be afraid to get a second opinion. It may be that your aging parent won't be any better off even with the operation. In that case, you'll have to make a big decision, one that you'll want to take a "majority rules" vote on with your family members. An operation on an elderly person like your parent is always a major life event. Do everything in your power to oversee the process. Be there to hold their hand when they are wheeled out of the operating room—even though they may be asleep.

An operation can leave your parent feeling confused. Don't expect them to start doing pushups or cartwheels right after their operation. But don't give up on them either. Always respect their dignity. Never talk about them as though they aren't there. Remember that they can often hear you even if they appear out of it. Be careful what you say about them, even if they're sleeping. Give your mom or dad the gift of your respect, and make sure that your family gets that message also.

Release from the Hospital

Sometimes older patients are discharged from the hospital to a nursing home. If your parent has been released, that usually signals the immediate crisis is over. The next stage is a period of convalescence. The nursing home serves as the halfway point before returning to "normal" life. Nursing homes are covered in more detail in the next chapter.

Take a few minutes to write a thank you letter to all the nurses and doctors who gave your parent special attention. Your appreciation may affect the way they care for the next person. Make sure you gather up all of your parent's belongings from the hospital room before they're moved. Valuables are usually bagged and kept in the hospital safe, so you'll need to get these also.

Usually, your parent will be transported to a nursing home by an ambulance provided by the hospital. Before this happens, be sure to read the next chapter so you can select a good nursing home before the hospital ships your parent to a home they have an "arrangement" with.

Many older people actually enjoy
their stay in nursing homes.

Chapter 6

NURSING HOMES

Many people associate nursing homes with times they visit their grandma or volunteer to sing Christmas carols for the residents. Unfortunately, not all of us have pleasant memories of nursing homes. They may conjure traumatic visits to a relative confined in a bed or wheelchair, muttering incoherent words or repeating the same phrase.

According to the Nursing Home Abuse Center, around 1.4 million people are living in nursing homes in the U.S., of those:

- 7.8% are 95 years old or older.

- 33.8% are 85-94 years old.

- 26.4% are 75-84 years old.

- 16.5% are 65-74 years old.

- 15.5% are younger than 65.

Many nursing homes house residents who suffer from cognitive disorders that make living by themselves impossible. Other patients may reside temporarily in the home as they recover from an illness, injury, or operation. Often, individuals in nursing homes require ongoing care with activities of daily living, including meal preparation, eating, bathing and dressing, hygiene, medications, and getting around.

My mom was referred to a nursing home straight from the hospital. Since my sister and I were ignorant about which nursing home would be best to send her to, the hospital chose one for us. Looking back, I don't think it was the best place for her. I remember my sister's eyes tightening as we walked in for the first time, "What's that smell?" she referred to the pervasive smell of dirty diapers that greeted us. It seemed to have worked its way into the ventilation system and into all our memories of that place. I pinched my nose.

When we made a request, the nursing staff often jabbered to each other in a foreign language. Sometimes, they'd even laugh, which made us feel distrustful. Did they have Mom's best interests in mind? Did they understand our requests and concerns? I didn't understand their English spoken with a strong accent. This became a huge barrier when they tried to explain something about Mom's condition. Or why she showed up with bruises one morning. I'm sure they got tired of me asking them to repeat their words over and over.

Don't be caught off guard like we were. Research nursing homes in your area beforehand. The Medicare website (www.medicare.gov/care-compare) has a nursing home section where you can search the ratings of the homes near your zip code. Check other online sites. Ask your friends. Call a few homes and see if they answer. Visit the most promising ones and use the Nursing Home Evaluation Checklist in this chapter to help you rate your choices. I recommend keeping at least three viable options in case your favorite isn't available when needed. It is best to have a pocket list at hand before your parent has to spend time in a nursing home.

Luckily, my mom was only in that nursing home for a few weeks while she recuperated from emergency colon surgery. There, she re-learned how to speak and swallow after her throat had been damaged from a respirator during surgery. The nursing home helped her get back on her feet again so she could return to the residential board and care facility she lived before the operation.

It was hard for us to see Mom in a nursing home, especially this one. Not just because the quality of her life was suffering, but also because we realized that from this point on, we'd be taking a more active role in her welfare and her finances. The burden of responsibility for her care finally dawned on us. We never expected that we'd have to pick a nursing home, but now she suffered from the result of our inaction. We were going to be stepping up and taking on a more active role in our parent's life. These are the parts of life few people talk about. By reading this book, you'll be better prepared to meet these challenges.

 ## When Nursing Homes Are Needed

1. **After a hospital discharge.** When your parent needs help with recovery that you cannot provide. This may include speech therapy, occupational therapy for personal care, assistance with eating, and physical therapy for walking and movement.

2. **On doctor's advice.** Their medical condition needs full-time skilled nursing care.

3. **When home care is no longer sufficient.** Your parent's condition is too much for the family to handle, and home health care services are more expensive than a nursing home.

4. **Serious mental illness.** Conditions such as dementia or psychosis require full-time care.

5. **Inability to care for basic needs.** When your parent cannot complete daily tasks such as bathing, dressing, bathroom activities, or brushing their hair or teeth.

6. **Loneliness and isolation.** When they require more professional attention, interaction, and companionship than they can get at home and have the means to pay for nursing home care.

What Nursing Homes Do

A nursing home aims to provide therapeutic care and treatment to return a patient to their highest level of physical, mental, and social well-being. These facilities offer high-maintenance care for people recovering from illness or operations. They also provide long-term nursing supervision for people with chronic medical problems. To be clear, a nursing home isn't a hospital. It can't provide surgical care for acute conditions as a hospital can. If your parent has been discharged from the hospital directly to a nursing home, Medicare will usually cover 100 days in the home for convalescence.

Nursing homes offer special care from qualified, trained nurses and visiting therapists. They provide a regimen of exercise, nutrition, and therapy to help your parent get back on their feet. Part of their job is to motivate your parent to recover so that they can, once again, lead an ordinary and fulfilling life without help from nurses.

Types of Nursing Homes

Acronyms that follow the name of health care facilities refer to the type of care they provide. Here are the types of homes and the acronyms that define them. When searching for a home, make sure it aligns with the care your parent is seeking.

1. **Intermediate Care Facility (ICF)**—provides long-term care with non-continuous skilled nursing care under a physician's direction. ICFs mainly provide custodial care for those with mental disabilities or declining health. An ICF provides less care than a skilled nursing facility but more than a residential care facility.

2. **Skilled Nursing Facility (SNF)**—provides 24-hour care and nursing supervision by registered and licensed vocational nurses. These facilities offer long- or short-term healthcare and assistance with many aspects of daily living. They also provide speech, occupational, and other therapy a patient needs for independent daily living.

3. **Skilled Nursing Facility Severe Disabilities (SNFSD)**—provides 24-hour care for people with severe mental disabilities. Many of

these facilities have locked or secure living areas for the patients' protection and the protection of others.

Selecting a Nursing Home

To protect patients, all states require licensing for nursing homes. State inspectors regularly visit to make sure they comply with state laws and Medicare and Medicaid regulations. Your goal should be to find the best nursing home that fits your parent's needs at the most affordable price. With typical prices of over $100,000 a year for a private room in a U.S. nursing home, it makes sense to do some shopping.

When the hospital sends your parent to a nursing home, they'll consider your insurance options. They will suggest you pick a nursing home covered by your parent's insurance plan or Medicare. If you haven't researched one, the hospital will choose one for you, as it did for my mother. Please don't make this mistake. When hospitals pick a nursing home for you, these homes may be places they have a "working relationship" with. Follow the guidelines listed below to find your parent a decent nursing home that can provide good care at a fair cost.

Shop Around

As mentioned earlier, check Medicare's Nursing Homes section (www. medicare.gov/care-compare). This website uses a 5-star rating system to classify the quality of care in a given Medicare-participating nursing home. This website should get you started on your search, but beware, many quality rating criteria could be self-reported by facilities. Check things out for yourself. Develop your own list of highly rated nursing homes near you from the website. Call them and ask how they would handle a specific need, such as a special diet request for more fiber or cranberry juice. How do they respond? Are they dismissive? Do they seem empathetic, well-informed, and caring? Do their answers seem satisfactory?

Plan Your Visit

Finding a facility close to your home may provide a sense of comfort and make visits more convenient. Bring a sibling or other close family members and plan to visit a few of these places during meal times, evening hours, or weekends. What you see during these off-hour periods can provide insight into their general vibe at a time when they're not fully staffed and looking their best. As you walk through the facility, try to imagine what it would feel like to an elderly patient. How would you feel about calling this home?

The *Nursing Home Evaluation Checklist* in *Figure 6-1* should help you keep track of how each home appears to you at the time of your visit. Make copies and use them for your final decision.

Nursing Home Evaluation Checklist

Name of facility _____

Type: ☐ ICF ☐ SNF ☐ SNFSD   Monthly cost _____

Address _____

Website _____ Phone _____

Environment

Location nearby? ① ② ③ ④ ⑤ _____

Smell? ① ② ③ ④ ⑤ _____

Rooms? ① ② ③ ④ ⑤ _____

Staff

Were your questions answered on initial phone call? ① ② ③ ④ ⑤

_____

Does the staff communicate well? ① ② ③ ④ ⑤ _____

Are staff respectful of the patients? ① ② ③ ④ ⑤ _____

Does staff offer assistance quickly? ① ② ③ ④ ⑤ _____

Do the attendants appear trustworthy? ① ② ③ ④ ⑤ _____

Meals

Dining area kept clean and orderly? ① ② ③ ④ ⑤ _____

A menu? ① ② ③ ④ ⑤ _____

Can residents eat in their room? ① ② ③ ④ ⑤ _____

Assistance with eating? ① ② ③ ④ ⑤ _____

Special diets accommodated? ① ② ③ ④ ⑤ _____

Access

Can you visit any time? ① ② ③ ④ ⑤ _____

A private area for visiting? ① ② ③ ④ ⑤ _____

Can you take your parent outside? ① ② ③ ④ ⑤ _____

Activities

Is there an appointed activities director? ① ② ③ ④ ⑤ _____

Does a space exist for activities? ① ② ③ ④ ⑤ _____

Can residents continue with their own hobbies? ① ② ③ ④ ⑤ _____

Privacy

Does staff knock on the door before entering a room? ① ② ③ ④ ⑤

_____

Can residents bathe or shower anytime? ① ② ③ ④ ⑤ _____

Personal

Can residents have their own laptops, phones? ① ② ③ ④ ⑤ _____

Do they have a policy on missing valuables? ① ② ③ ④ ⑤ _____

Medical

Does a nurse administer daily medications? ① ② ③ ④ ⑤ _____

Can residents keep non-prescription drugs? ① ② ③ ④ ⑤ _____

Can your parent keep their own doctor? ① ② ③ ④ ⑤ _____

Services

Salon or personal grooming available? ① ② ③ ④ ⑤ _____

Emergency dentistry available? ① ② ③ ④ ⑤ _____

Is there a specific person to call about your parent's status? ① ② ③ ④ ⑤

_____

Will you be involved in the daily/weekly reviews of care? ① ② ③ ④ ⑤

_____

Figure 6-1 *Nursing Home Evaluation Checklist*

After conducting a reconnaissance tour, you may be so delightfully impressed that you decide to return for an official tour. Call and make an appointment with the staff or marketing manager for the complete tour package. Nursing homes may look similar, but you'll be looking for the subtle things that can identify the exceptional from the usual.

1. **Don't be too impressed by the lobby.** It's only a façade built to impress. Look at the site's interior. Do the residents appear happy? Does the staff interact with them, or do they appear rushed? Do they seem to know each other by name? Are the residents talking to each other?

2. **Let your nose be your guide.** Do you smell feces, urine, bleach, vinegar, or Pine-sol? The smell of dirty diapers could indicate that the staff is too busy to care for incontinent patients quickly enough or that soiled garments are not disposed of properly. The pungent smell of bleach or disinfectant could indicate that the facility is hiding these odors.

3. **Are there enough windows?** Many facilities don't allow fresh air to enter and leave residents to breathe stale recycled air. Is there access to fresh air?

4. **How do the rooms look?** Can they be personalized? Can they be private? Or are they shared?

5. **Does the staff speak English as a second language?** The U.S. imports nurses from other countries to fulfill low-paying nursing jobs. They are often fantastic, competent nurses, but the day may come when you'll have to communicate when your parent's life is in the balance.

6. **Are there live outings or activities to increase socialization?** Are there planned activities? Or are the patients left on their bed to watch TV in their rooms?

7. **Are residents being restrained?** Nursing home reform laws ban the use of physical or drug-induced "restraints." Do residents appear to be happy or overly drugged?

8. **Check out the daily meals/menu.** Attendants usually help patients with meals. Do they seem to have a caring relationship with the patients?

9. **Talk to a resident.** Once you're out of range of a nurse or orderly, chat with one or two residents about how they feel about being there.

10. **Is a doctor available at all times in case of emergency?** Does the doctor have to be called, or is one on staff at the facility?

11. **What kind of day-to-day dental care is available?** Is there some care for brushing, flossing, and denture cleaning? Or does it cost extra?

12. **Lost items.** How do they address a resident's lost personal possessions? Do they have prevention measures or protocols for theft?

13. **Ask about family councils.** These are groups formed of patients' family members that work to communicate concerns to facility administrators. If there is a family council, ask for the contact person's email or phone number and find out their opinion.

Making Your Parent Comfortable

If you can, visit nursing homes with your parent and make this choice ahead of time. That way, you'll be fully prepared when and if you need it. If you're not able to convince your parent to do this with you, do your recon work with a sibling or two when your parent is in the hospital. When you've finally settled on a facility you like, meet with the administrators and sign the paperwork. Communicate your preferences to the hospital's discharge planning staff and physician. The ambulance will move your parent to the home upon discharge from the hospital. It's essential to try and be there when your parent arrives. To help them adjust, bring some photos or familiar items and place them around the room. Bring their bathrobe, slippers, and comfortable shoes. Mark their initials in permanent marker on the labels of their clothes, as they can get mixed up in the facility's laundry.

Visit Often

Once your parent is settled, try to visit at least once a week. Coordinate with family members, so you don't all arrive on the same night. If you can't often visit, set up a device to Facetime them during your initial visit, or call them and ask about their day. If you're out of state or on vacation, try encouraging relatives in the area to visit. Bring the kids. Just about everyone I saw in a nursing home really enjoyed seeing children. Let your parent have the right to brag about their grandchildren to the other patients. Allowing children to see people at an advanced age can be an enlightening teaching moment.

This is also probably a good time to have any heart-to-heart talks that you've been putting off. Reassure your parent that you're rooting for their recovery and mention that you're looking forward to being with them in the future. Thank them for what they've done for you. Also, tell them everything you've been holding in as if there's no tomorrow. That day may come faster than you expect, and you certainly don't want to be harboring any regrets at this stage in their life.

Get to Know the Nurses

You should always respect the nurses and attendants who watch over your parent. Establish a rapport with them. Bring them cookies, fruit, or coffee. Show concern. Ask about your parent's progress. The nurses will usually respond to your questions.

Having a good relationship with the nurses will come in handy when you have a problem and small problems *do* arise. I learned that it's better to bring minor issues to the attention of the person responsible rather than immediately complaining to someone higher up the ladder. When an attendant doesn't change a diaper on time, don't report them right away. Speak to them directly. Mention your concern and show you respect them, yet depend on them to get it done. If the problem continues, then it's time to bring it to the attention of the head nurse.

Handling Major Problems and Concerns

If you feel there's a major issue, for example, your parent is being ignored or placed in isolation, and their physical and emotional needs aren't being met, ask for a meeting with the head nurse to discover what's going on. There are usually two sides to every story, and your parent may only be relaying only one side to you. It's wise to investigate with a fair yet firm attitude. Perhaps you can pave the way for better communication between your parent and the staff.

If the problem is major, you can always contact the National Citizens for Nursing Home Reform (www.nursinghomeaction.org). They are a national consumer voice for quality long-term care and can help you take the appropriate action.

Attending Assessment Meetings

By law, a nursing home must complete a full evaluation of the resident's condition within 14 days of admission and at least once every 12 months. The initial care planning meeting is a good time for you to let the facility know your parent's likes and dislikes, habits, and lifestyle before moving to the nursing home. If the staff knows more about their background, they can better meet their preferences and make the nursing home more tolerable.

A new assessment should be done within 14 days of any significant change in your parent's physical or mental condition. During these meetings, the staff and the therapist meet to discuss your parent's condition. During later assessments, they'll explain how your parent's rehabilitation is progressing. This is an important meeting that you should be part of. Try and have at least one family member attend with you. Be punctual, and don't be afraid to ask questions. You're in an advocacy role. Make sure that you have a clear understanding of your parent's condition and prognosis by the time you leave the meeting.

 Sample Assessment Meeting Questions

- Is my parent making progress on their recovery?
- Were there any complications? If so, what were they caused by?
- Are the therapies showing progress? Will these be changing?
- What can I do to help in my parent's progress or care?
- When can my parent return home or to a care facility offering greater independence?
- What kind of follow-up care will be needed?

Helping with Rehabilitation

Nursing homes provide therapy to get your parent back into normal mode. These therapies typically include speech and occupational aid to help them talk and groom themselves. They'll also usually provide physical therapy, so their muscles can regain strength. The therapists will usually ask that you help in the rehabilitation. Walk with your parent if you can. Call them and talk with them often. Ask directly how you can help in your parent's recovery. If you can't meet with the therapist, call them. They'll usually appreciate your concern. You may fill in some of the blanks in your parent's background to help with the treatment.

Nursing Home Expenses

As mentioned earlier, nursing home care can be expensive. Currently, Medicare will cover most expenses of some nursing home care for the first 100 days if specific requirements are met. Supplemental insurance plans can help make up some of the extra costs. But after the initial period is up, your parent's nest egg may quickly diminish unless they've prepared for this ahead of time. You may want to figure out how your parent will be paying for this and how to protect their assets. Read on for some possible solutions.

Long-term Insurance

If your parent is in the small minority of people with long-term care insurance, they've done their homework and are in good shape financially. Alert the nursing home administrator, and your worries will be taken care of. Unfortunately, not many people carry long-term care insurance as premiums start out around $2,500 a year for a couple in their 50s. By the time they reach age 70, the rates typically grow to over $14,000 a year. Not everyone can afford expensive payments on insurance they may never use. There are other ways of affording long-term care within your parent's means. You just have to think creatively, weigh the options, and make some hard and very difficult choices.

Exploring Possible Sources of Financing

Take a look at your parent's finances on their Personal Financial Worksheet from Chapter 3. Try to figure out some safe ways to make these assets generate enough income to help pay for your parent's stay in a nursing home. Here are a few ideas to get you started:

- **Home Rental:** If they have a home, consider renting it out furnished to generate temporary income for their nursing home stay. Consider short-term renting as an Air B&B. This way, you or someone you hire can manage it to generate income while the property value continues to grow; plus, your parent has a home to return to should they want. Check rental and Air B&B prices online for your area and local ordinances. Calculate if the rental income generated from their house and any pensions, dividends, social security income, and interest generated from their nest egg can get them a bed in a nursing home or the long-term facility of their choice.

- **Sell the Car:** If they have a car, there's a good possibility they may not need it anymore. Discuss it with them and, if necessary, sell it. Advertise it as a low-mileage car, driven by an older person who drove slowly and carefully, and get a premium price. Tell potential buyers you're using the money to help fund your parent's stay in a nursing home. If the buyer tries to negotiate with you, take them to meet your parent and make them feel ashamed. Don't laugh. This technique worked for me. I remember how the buyer's face dropped when we walked into the nursing home, and I asked Mom if she'd go down on the price. "Heck no!" she replied incredulously from her bed. The buyer glanced at me, and I could see he finally believed my story. I still sold her car for the full price.

- **Other Assets:** Do they have an RV? A vacation home? A musical instrument or a rare stamp collection? Any jewelry or other valuables that could be sold for nursing home payments?

The Nursing Home Financial Spiral
As of this writing, Medicare and your supplemental insurance will pay for 100 days of recovery in a nursing home if your parent arrives from a hospital. If your parent only has Medicare, they will still have to pay around

$200 per day after day 20 in the home. After the 100-day period ends, costs soar to the nursing home per diem cost. Medicare laws do change, and this may not be such a problem in the future. Always check the Medicare website (www.medicare.gov).

If your parent only lives on a small pension and Social Security, you'll have to figure out how they'll pay. An owned house can be sold or rented out to help fund the costs. Using their house as a rental to pay for medical bills may work in their favor should they apply for Medicaid. They may be able to keep the home as one of their last assets if it can generate income. If they have non-income generating assets, you may have to start depleting them monthly until Medicaid kicks in and pays the bills. For more information, check the Medicaid website (www.medicaid.gov).

 ## Medicaid

Medicaid is the medical safety net for those with no assets. So it is also hailed as the last rung of the social safety net. It is a federal program operated by states, and each has different eligibility requirements that change over time. States have the option to establish a "medically needy program" for individuals with significant health needs but whose income is too high to otherwise qualify for Medicaid. Medically needy individuals can still become eligible by "spending down" the amount of income above a state's medically needy income standard. Individuals spend down by incurring medical and remedial care expenses for which they do not have health insurance.

Once an individual's incurred expenses exceed the difference between the individual's income and the state's medically needy income level (the "spend down" amount), the person can be eligible for Medicaid. The Medicaid program then pays the cost of services that exceed the individual's expenses to become eligible. For more information on your state's eligibility requirements, go to Medicaid's State Resources (www.medicaid.gov/resources-for-states/index.html).

Asset Protection

Ideally, when you set up your parent's Trust, as covered in Chapter 3, you have planned how to protect your parent's assets for long-term care. Each state has different laws regarding the "spend down" of assets to be eligible for Medicaid. An asset protection lawyer in the state your parent resides in should be your best guide on how to protect their assets from the state and Medicaid.

Moral Considerations

Your parent's money belongs to them. They earned it, and they saved it. Even though you may have ideas about protecting assets or rewarding yourself for helping your parent, you have no right to the money at this point. You are in the driver's seat of the Trust-mobile. You are obligated to steer in the direction that represents your parent's best interest and their wants and needs. If they have an utterly fool-hearted idea, pull together your siblings and try and have them help bring your parent into reality. Many times in caring for an aging parent, difficult decisions will seem like thankless tasks. Try and keep the highest standards of behavior so that no one, including yourself, will ever be able to question your honesty on your choices. If you have questions, bring your siblings into the decision-making process. If you do your best, you'll still have your integrity intact when it's over.

Nursing Home Alternatives

You may want to consider the options for care that are not as expensive as nursing home care. They may not offer the same level of care as a nursing home but can be good choices.

At-Home Nurse Care and Family Members

An alternative to nursing homes would be to have someone come to your parent's house to care for them. If your parent needs specialized care, at-home nurses could come to your parent's home and provide one-on-one care, either part-time or full-time. On the other hand, family members can step in if your parent's needs are more general. A non-skilled family member can provide live-in services, help shop, prepare meals, or other services like house cleaning or yard work. With this arrangement, your parent receives part-time care from a nurse and family member in a familiar environment. The downside is the lack of built-in social interaction with people your parent's age they'd have in a nursing home.

Religious Nursing Homes

You may find less-expensive nursing homes provided by specific church organizations. Your parent doesn't necessarily have to be a member to be accepted. Besides offering excellent care at an affordable price, these organizations may focus on doing good for your parent rather than making a profit off them. From what I've seen, the staff and administrators are often honest and helpful. The only downside is that if your parent is not religious, these facilities may not be their "cup of tea." Also, sometimes the facilities are not the most modern.

Don't Expect an Overnight Cure

When your elderly parent endures an illness, surgery, or mishap that lands them in a nursing home, it may take a while before you begin to see improvements. Older people heal more slowly than younger ones. It's not easy watching the one who cared for you for much of your life end up in a nursing home. You may feel guilty about not spending enough time with them—especially if you're already juggling a career and family. You may get that feeling that their time is coming to a close. That's why it is crucial to make the most of your visits. Remind your parent that you love them, care for them, and that you're there to help them get better.

Nursing homes are meant for rehabilitation. To me, they'd make expensive and depressing retirement homes. The more you can help your parent get through the rehabilitation process positively, the faster they'll be on the road to recovery. Much of that process involves your support in being there and maintaining a positive mental outlook. Joining a support group may help in this, and many nursing homes offer them. You can also convey your feelings to family members who are good at listening and responding.

Sometimes taking your parent to a nursing home can serve as the necessary catalyst that brings your family closer. You might be surprised when a positive experience arises from this sad event. If that happens, try and build on that positive emotion so that your parent is aware of it and can benefit from it. That positive emotion can help you through practically any sadness. As your parent's advocate, make their time in a nursing home serve one purpose—to get better! Point out the possibilities that await them when they're discharged and help them in their re-entry to familiar surroundings.

Soon Mom became suspicious and
paranoid about her neighbors.

Chapter 7
DEALING WITH DEMENTIA

Dementia is an insidious disease. It's so sneaky that you may not even see the mental decline of your parent until they exhibit signs of paranoia or delusions. These afflictions frequently piggyback on the effects of dementia. This chapter should help you identify dementia and other mental problems in your parent and help you find ways of dealing with them.

My mom taught school most of her life. She was highly organized and independent. Retired, Mom still read constantly and became adept at oil painting. At 76, she moved into a trailer park in my city to be closer to my sister and me. However, her canvases and brushes never emerged from her moving boxes after that move. I bought her a video player that Christmas, hoping that watching movies would help her shake off her newly-found disinterest in life. But the player sat untouched, unless I happened to arrive with a film in hand. Likewise, the microwave I'd gotten also sat idle, another piece of unused new technology. At the time, I didn't realize that her ability to learn new things was diminishing or that this behavior was indicative of dementia.

However, when Mom became suspicious and paranoid about her neighbors, I realized something was up.

"They can see into my window," she hissed as she pulled her curtains. "I've seen them looking."

"Really?" I asked, uncertain.

"Yes." She elaborated on her story and convinced me that she needed a barrier to block the neighbor's view. I thought it was strange, but Mom had always been a little paranoid anyway. So, I built a fence. I figured her paranoia came from living through the Great Depression when people couldn't trust banks and kept their money in jars buried in the ground (according to her). I rationalized that if I built a fence, she'd finally open her curtains and let some light in on those darkened rooms. I couldn't see the obvious—that her paranoia was growing.

Mom had sometimes suffered bouts of depression. Now her dark mood returned with a vengeance. Figuring she was lonely, my sister and I decided she needed more socialization. We talked her into moving to a lively retirement community. This worked well for a while. She made new friends and went on social outings. The symptoms of depression and paranoia retreated, but only temporarily. Soon, she insisted that we change her bank accounts because she thought her money was missing. She accused the bank of taking things from her safety deposit box. She became absurdly paranoid about my brother-in-law, who she suspected had a master key to her apartment. Anything out-of-place or missing was blamed on the poor guy. He was flummoxed and also hurt. She used to trust him and got along well with him. For some reason, she singled him out as a bad guy.

The remarkable part of all this is that my sister and I rolled with the "new normal" and denied Mom's behavior was odd—even while helping her change banking accounts and the locks on her apartment. We never suspected that dementia was taking her away from us. We figured it was normal for people to grow strange as they neared 80.

Symptoms of dementia start slowly. Often, they're mixed in with periods of what appears to be rational thinking and behavior. So, just when it appeared that Mom was heading off the deep end, she'd return with what was complete clarity, asking us about our spouses and offering up the motherly advice we'd grown up with and trusted. In hindsight, I can clearly see the progression of the disorder. But at the time, it snuck in and stole Mom from us without a clue. Well, maybe there were signs that things were amiss, but because we were busy raising our kids and working (and perhaps a little in denial), we didn't see them until it was too late.

Now, I can see that my denial was rooted in fear. Mom had brought me up and shaped my reality. If my mother was demented, I must be demented too. Although some people might find her actions weird, I didn't want an official confirmation that she was, in fact, "crazy." I really wanted her to be "normal" so that I could feel normal. I could just imagine everyone at my work hearing the news and moving their fingers in circles around their ears while nodding at me and saying, "Ah-ha! That explains it!" This may be an irrational feeling, but it's sad and even scary when someone we love and trust begins to change. Especially when they don't realize they're changing.

We took Mom to doctor after doctor, trying to find a cure. Was it low potassium? Could it be a urinary tract infection? Each doctor drew countless pints of blood. None of them seemed to be able to tell us what was wrong. We worried it might be dementia. What would we do then? Eventually, a friend pointed us in the right direction and recommended a geriatric advisor who suggested we take her for a geriatric evaluation at a local hospital.

Identifying Dementia and Other Mental Problems

Dementia is *not* a normal part of aging. It is caused by damage to brain cells and affects thinking, behavior, and feelings. Dementia opens the door for other mental conditions as the older brain compensates for the lack of memory and begins to act more on impulse. Soon, confusion, delusions, paranoia, and other mental disorders come along for the ride and make the condition even more complicated. At the current time, there is no perfect test for the wide range of mental conditions classified as dementia. But there are some ways to determine if dementia is impacting your parent's life. The checklist in *Figure 7-1* may help you identify any unusual behavior as warning signs of dementia or mental illness.

At the time of this writing, there is no cure for dementia. Lifestyle changes, such as dietary and physical exercise, can supplement what medications cannot and may boost your parent's quality of life.

Dietary changes, like increasing the intake of foods such as avocados, blueberries, and turmeric, have shown through research to slow the cognitive decline brought about by dementia. Exercise has been shown to produce a hormone (BDNF) known to battle dementia that significantly improves cognitive ability. A 2014 study published in JAMA showed that seniors who exercised frequently had 33% fewer cognitive defects.

Warning Signs of Dementia or Mental Illness

Everyone has unique traits in their personality. As your parent ages, these quirky idiosyncrasies may become more apparent. This may become especially true as your parent relies more on you to clean up their messes, straighten their checkbooks, or get them out of contracts they've signed. Dementia may be at the core of these problems. No one is immune to memory lapses, a moment of confusion, or misunderstandings. But certain behaviors stand out and signal the possibility of a disorder. Some of these are listed below. If you can check several of them, you may want to talk to your siblings about getting your parent for an evaluation.

☐ Resistance to learning new things.

☐ Unsubstantiated suspicions about missing money, neighbors, or friends.

☐ Leaving repeated text or phone messages about the same subject.

☐ Recalling memories that are blatantly false.

☐ Repeatedly asking the same question, even though you've given the answer.

☐ Extreme mood swings, like crying and laughing several times within an hour.

☐ Paying bills more than once, or not at all.

☐ Putting words in a sentence that don't belong. Mixing up their words.

☐ Calling you or other family members by names that aren't right.

☐ Complete loss of interest in a hobby or activity that was once dear to them.

☐ Letting you take the lead on a walk so they can find their way home.

☐ Consistent problems balancing the checkbook.

☐ Lack of appetite or change in eating habits.

Figure 7-1 *Warning Signs of Dementia or Mental Illness*

Most Common Types of Dementia

According to the Alzheimer's Association, 11.3%, or one in nine people aged 65 and older, has Alzheimer's Dementia. Alzheimer's accounts for 50-60% of dementia cases. Lewy Bodies Dementia is second, accounting for 15 to 25% of all cases. Vascular Dementia ranks third. According to the Alzheimer's Association, dementia kills 33% of seniors. That's more than heart disease or any single factor.

You've probably heard of or known someone with Alzheimer's disease. This most prevalent form of dementia presents the most severe symptoms. Patients undergo personality changes and tend to wander, requiring locked facilities.

The longer you live, the more your chances of contracting Alzheimer's disease. According to the Alzheimer's Association, 72% of Alzheimer's patients are 75 and over. Deaths from Alzheimer's disease have increased by 145% between 2000 and 2019. New research is always looking for a cure for Alzheimer's, as it represents the lion's share of dementia patients. Unfortunately, as of this writing, medications only seem to slow down the progression, and many have significant side effects.

Lewy Bodies Dementia typically affects males between 60 and 80 years old. The disease comes on quickly, with episodes where the afflicted cannot focus on one idea or task. This may include major psychiatric episodes that include hallucinations. Sometimes there is difficulty with body movement, causing the patient to fall and lose consciousness. At one time, it was believed that this form of dementia was related to Parkinson's disease because the symptoms were similar.

Vascular Dementia is caused by tiny strokes in the brain called infarctions. The symptoms are similar to Alzheimer's. However, afflicted patients have fewer tendencies to wander and undergo fewer personality changes than Alzheimer's patients.

Many times, dementia may be diagnosed as a combination of diseases. For instance, my mother's dementia was eventually diagnosed as caused by infarctions. This was determined by CAT scans, but she also showed indications of Alzheimer's disease. This diagnosis would imply that there were also plaques and tangles in her brain related to Alzheimer's disease, along with tiny strokes.

While no single test can diagnose Alzheimer's disease, a geriatric evaluation contains a battery of tests that can diagnose it. A clinical diagnosis can be 80-90% accurate and can help you understand the cause of dementia, which may even be reversible if caused by a drug reaction, tumor, infection, thyroid problem, or nutritional deficiencies. If the dementia is diagnosed as irreversible, the clinical diagnosis may at least help you find treatable factors that could be compounding the problem.

It's very typical to resist taking your parent for a clinical evaluation. Knowing what takes place in the evaluation process at a geriatric evaluation clinic may help you overcome this resistance. Getting your parent to the doctor is your first step.

Types of Dementia

There are many types of dementia. Here is some information on the more prevalent forms.

- **Alzheimer's Disease** is caused by a buildup of tangles and plaques in the brain. It makes people confused about where they are, have problems speaking or holding consistent thoughts, show poor judgment, and have dramatic mood and personality changes.

- **Vascular Dementia** is often caused by "mini" or "silent" strokes. The results of vascular dementia are often poor judgment, problems in planning and organizing, recognizing familiar places, becoming confused and agitated, and frequently falling when walking.

- **Lewy Bodies Dementia** is named after the scientist who discovered microscopic deposits of a particular protein that forms in the brains of affected patients. The results are an inability to make decisions or pay attention, visual hallucinations, unusual sleepiness during the day, periods of "blanking out," problems with movement such as trembling, slowness, and trouble walking, and violent dreams that include sleepwalking, talking, and punching.

- **Parkinson's Disease Dementia** affects 50% to 80% of the people with Parkinson's disease. The symptoms often develop years after the onslaught of Parkinson's. The symptoms are very similar to Lewy Bodies Dementia: stiff muscles, a shunted walk, a stooped posture, and a lack of facial expressions.

- **Frontotemporal Dementia** derives from damage in the front of the brain that controls planning, judgment, emotions, speech, and movement. The symptoms often involve personality changes, sudden lack of inhibitions in social situations, difficulty finding the right words when speaking, shakiness, balance problems, and muscle spasms.

- **Huntington's Disease** is a brain disorder caused by a genetic defect. The symptoms don't become apparent until age 30 to 50. The result

is the same as most other dementia: problems with thinking, planning, and concentration.

- **Creutzfeldt-Jakob Disease** is a relatively rare type of dementia
named after the scientist who discovered it. The disease is caused
by proteins in the brain that start folding into abnormal shapes. The
symptoms happen suddenly and quickly worsen, causing memory
and concentration problems, poor judgment, confusion, twitching
and muscle control problems, and trouble sleeping.

- **Normal Pressure Hydrocephalus** is caused by a buildup of fluid in
the brain from fluid in the spine. It can be caused by head trauma,
infection, tumor, or complications from surgery. The symptoms
include problems walking, impaired bladder control, trouble thinking and concentrating, and personality and behavior changes. Some
symptoms can be treated by draining the extra fluid from the brain.

- **Mixed Dementia** is a combination of two types of dementia. The
most common one is Alzheimer's disease and vascular dementia.

Immediate Action

By this point, you should have set up the important papers mentioned in
Chapter 3: Power of Attorney for Health Care, Durable Power of Attorney,
Life and Death Directives, and a good Trust of your parent's choice. Hope-
fully, you've also discussed a strategy for asset protection.

If you haven't already, as mentioned in Chapter 2, get your parent to a
doctor as part of a thorough physical examination. If you feel certain that
your parent has problems with memory-related issues, ask them what time
and date it is. Ask them to draw a clock showing 3:15. The clock test is a
straightforward test for dementia. Make sure the doctor checks the potassium level in their blood. Sometimes low potassium can alter memory and
cognitive ability. Bring a list of your parent's prescription drugs with you
to present to the doctor. Sometimes a combination of two drugs can also

lead to cognitive problems in older people.

The blood test should also check for syphilis, which seems absolutely ludicrous, but since the disease can produce dementia, it must be completely ruled out so the doctor can go on to the next possible cause. Giving approval for this test is the start of what you may feel are the little indignities that occur when your parent is suspected of having dementia. Your parent's doctor may start to speak more to you than your parent as you'll be relied on to take the lead in their decisions. As you leave the office, always ask your parent how they felt about the experience. Give them every chance to voice their feelings while they still can. Let them vent their frustrations and resistance.

Memory Field Test

The doctor may perform what is known as a "memory field test." They'll explain three items that your parent should remember and recall later during casual conversation. In Mom's case, the doctor presented three simple items: Elvis, a pink Cadillac, and a birthday cake.

He then went on about what activities he did that weekend. Suddenly, he looked at Mom, changed his tone, and asked, "Who's the current President?" Mom looked flummoxed but managed to spit out the answer after a few minutes. Then he asked kindly, tilting his head slightly, "What year is it?" Mom couldn't recall. He then looked concerned and asked, "Who is the Vice President?" She couldn't answer that one either. Then he delivered the final question: "Now remember those three key items that I asked you to remember? What were they?" After a few hints, the doctor spoke like Elvis, "One was a person's name, thank you very much." Thankfully, Mom remembered Elvis but completely forgot the pink Cadillac and the birthday cake. My sister and I were shaken that she'd failed such a simple memory test.

The doctor wasn't. He sat down and held his palms out as if asking, "What do we do now?" I raised my brows and glanced at my sister. She seemed frustrated as well. We'd hoped for a diagnosis of some kind. The doctor suggested that Mom was getting old and maybe a little forgetful. But my sister asked, "Mom has high blood pressure. Can we at least get a CAT scan or an MRI to see if she's had a stroke?" I'm glad she suggested this. This was the third doctor we'd been to trying to diagnose Mom's condition, and we weren't getting anywhere.

The doctor reluctantly agreed. A CAT scan or MRI can find undetected strokes. Mom had high blood pressure for as long as I could remember. It was possible that as her arteries hardened with age, small pieces could have broken off and caused tiny clots in her brain. These could have caused micro-strokes, called infarctions, that starved the brain of blood in certain areas and caused dementia. We scheduled a CAT scan and found that micro-strokes had occurred in Mom's brain.

Although primary physicians should be the ones referring elderly patients to an official geriatric evaluation, none of the doctors we visited brought it up. We only found out about a geriatric evaluation through a friend. If your parent displays signs of dementia, ask your doctor about a geriatric evaluation.

Geriatric Assessment Evaluation

The geriatric assessment is a multidisciplinary assessment by specialists designed to evaluate an older person's functional ability, physical health, cognition, and mental health. It examines nutrition, vision, hearing, and balance. The geriatric assessment aids in diagnosing medical conditions, treatments, follow-up plans, and an evaluation of long-term care needs. Best of all, if your parent is on Medicare, as of this writing, the test is free.

The evaluation takes place in a hospital where your parent stays for several days while undergoing physical and psychiatric tests by a team of doctors. They assess your parent's condition, prescribe drugs, and help you plan for your parent's future care.

Your parent may resist going to a hospital for testing. Most elderly people enjoy their independence and don't want to think about losing their freedom. They may be reluctant, as my mom was, to find out the truth of their condition. Be gentle and remind them (if your doctor referred them) that this is what the doctor wants. I had to go with, "Let's get a professional evaluation, so you can feel better." It worked with Mom, and she actually enjoyed all the attention from the doctors.

Leaving your parent in a geriatric hospital for two days won't be easy on you. The guilt may creep in, but this is your responsibility to follow a practical path for their best care. Consult with your family members, as necessary.

How the Exam is Conducted

While your parent is in the hospital, they'll be diagnosed by a trained staff of around five people who will interview, test, and examine them. They'll provide blood tests, neurological examinations, and laboratory tests like an electroencephalogram to record activity in the brain, a CAT scan, and possibly an MRI of their brain.

After these examinations, they'll probably administer a series of psychiatric evaluations to ensure that your parent isn't suffering from depression or any other psychiatric ailment that mimics the effects of dementia. They'll perform psychometric tests to determine your parent's areas of impairment and of remaining strength. They'll also test your parent's ability to perform routine tasks necessary for living independently.

The staff will check over the prescription and non-prescription drugs your parent is taking—especially looking for any drug combinations that could cause an adverse reaction. Be sure and bring your parent's drug list you prepared in Chapter 2.

If the gathered data results in a mental disorder diagnosis, they'd prescribe drugs to achieve normalcy so that your parent can function independently on their own. If your parent has dementia, these medications can help with the frustration of losing their memory and alleviate conditions like hallucinations and paranoia. This may help your parent enjoy more of the time they have left. That is a critical function, as the average lifespan after diagnosis of dementia is four to eight years, depending on their age and how soon the diagnoses were given. Eventually, they will become frail, incontinent, subject to strokes, and a weakened immune response. They are also more likely to choke on their food as they forget to swallow, which can lead to pneumonia.

When I visited my mom at the clinic, she was happy. She appreciated the attention from all the doctors as they tested new drug therapies on her. When she was discharged, I had to call the doctors and have them cut back on the dosage. Mom had grown quiet and lost her ability to talk much. Don't hesitate to bring doctors up to date on your parent's condition after discharge. They'll usually be happy to work with you.

Learning to Live with the Stigma

Degenerative brain disorders can conjure up a lot of horrible images. Visit a few Alzheimer's nursing homes, and you'll quickly understand what I mean. By accident, my sister and I visited a locked wing of a nursing home, and a lady begged us to take her out of there. "I swear, there's nothing wrong with me!" The woman literally cried while tugging at my sleeve. She begged to leave with us. Eventually, the attendants came and led her gently away, but that experience sure shook us up.

The stigma of Alzheimer's and dementia is so strong you may not want to face the fact that someone you love has it. You may want to pretend (as we did and her doctor did also) that they just have a little memory problem that comes and goes. Unfortunately, if that little problem is left untreated, it only gets worse. You've got to take action before they take their nest egg out of the bank, bury it in a jar and forget where. You won't want them wandering around lost in the heat or the cold.

When your parent is diagnosed with dementia, you'll no longer have doubts. However, you may still have trouble accepting this new reality. You may feel a sense of loss like your parent has died yet is still living. It's hard to accept that the one who once took care of you is now in your care.

Support Groups

Consider joining a support group. Looking back, I sure wish I had. You can learn how others are coping with the same situation and share in the laughter and the tears of their experiences. I was feeling pretty low until I met up with an old friend who shared his experience of his mom, who developed full-blown Alzheimer's. When his mom met a guy at a nursing home, she immediately wanted to marry him to satisfy her newly-found morals, so she could have sex. My friend was aghast. The potential groom was indigent, while his mom still had assets his family was desperately trying to preserve. The solution was to plan a pretend wedding to satisfy his mom's desires. All his siblings gathered and arranged this play-act in the nursing home rec room, down to the decorations and even a wedding cake. Hearing his story made me identify with his pain and laugh at his solution, which felt good when Mom's diagnosis seemed hopeless. We can often find humor in the story of other people's struggles and realize that we're not alone.

 ## Where to Find Support Groups

Caregiver support groups are often underutilized because people often think they don't have the time or feel self-conscious about speaking about personal subjects with strangers. A well-functioning support group offers a chance for a group of strangers facing common issues to meet to share their experiences, and offer support, encouragement, and comfort to each other.

Support groups offer the best medicine—the voice of people walking on the same path. The group can provide you with a safe place to get practical, constructive, and helpful information. You'll have the benefit of encouragement, and you'll learn more about coping with your problems through sharing the experiences of others. Listening to how others have faced their challenges can also make you feel less alone in your difficulties.

You can often find a group from the social work department of hospitals. Ask the doctors of the geriatric evaluation for a few leads. Call your local adult day care services for tips. Some large faith-based organizations offer support groups for caregivers.

Support Groups for Dementia Caregivers

At one time, most of these groups met in person. Today, many groups exist on Facebook, or Zoom, while fewer still meet in person. You might want to find out who the facilitator is, the organizing principle, and a little about the group's makeup before joining. That will give you a better understanding of what to expect.

Facebook Groups

A quick search on Facebook using the search terms below can help you locate encouraging support groups.

- *Support group for dementia caregivers*
- *Caring for elderly parents*
- *Dementia caregivers support group*
- *Alzheimer's and dementia caregivers support*
- *Caregiver's support group*

ZOOM Groups

Zoom and other online platforms helped people connect during the COVID pandemic and offered the convenience of connecting face-to-face with others through online media. Online groups provide the convenience of joining others who live miles away from the comfort of your living room. Type "Zoom groups for caregivers," and a plethora of groups show up. A few are listed below.

- **The Alzheimer's Family Care Group** (www.afscenter.org) offers a Zoom group to help caregivers. To find out more, go to their official website.

- **Missoula Aging Services** (www.missoulaagingservices.org) has a Caregivers Zoom Support Group. To find out more, go to their website.

- **Family Caregiver Alliance** sponsors several Zoom support groups at www.caregiver.org

Advanced Housing Needs

Just before Mom was discharged from her geriatric evaluation, I got a call from one of the doctors. "Your mom is unable to take care of herself and is going to need 24-hour care. She can't return to where she's living," he announced. My mind reeled. Before the evaluation, she was staying in an independent living facility, and I assumed she was okay. How could my sister or I provide 24-hour care for her? She could move to the assisted living section of her retirement home. Still, it would cost more than her teachers' pension provided, and her savings would be rapidly depleted.

"How should we handle that? Any ideas?" I asked the doctor, clutching at straws.

"Start looking around," he advised.

I called my sister, who was as distressed and confused as I on how to handle this new development. We had one weekend to find another place that offered help with bathing, hygiene, and 24-hour care. Remembering the facilities with the locked doors and wandering, confused patients, especially the lady who held on to my arm and begged me to free her, haunted us. I sure wouldn't want Mom to go there.

Then the phone rang. "I understand you're looking for a home that offers 24-hour care," the voice boomed as if a gift from God. It was music to our ears. That discharge doctor must have made some calls for us. Soon we were visiting a residential facility in a nearby town that offered 24-hour care for a small group of patients in a family setting. Meals, bathing, and dispensing of drugs were all included. Best of all, they had a room available, and it fits into what Mom could afford. Moving her that weekend wasn't easy, though. She'd look up at us carrying in the boxes to her new home and say, "I want to go home." But when I asked her where home was, she couldn't seem to remember.

I told her she only had to stay at her new place "a little bit longer." Your parent may respond to a similar phrase. It only took a few days before she forgot her old friends and familiar surroundings at the retirement home and settled into the new, smaller residence. She stopped asking us to take her home. Despite that, it took longer for my sister and I to get over our feelings of guilt for having moved her.

Dealing with the Decline

Mom left the doors of the geriatric assessment facility in a wheelchair. She was vomiting periodically, a side effect of donepezil (Aricept) prescribed to slow dementia. Current medications cannot completely stop dementia, but some can relieve some symptoms and slow its path. No drug comes without possible side effects, but we were worried about dehydration and how weak the Aricept might make her. Also, she looked worse than when she entered the assessment facility. Did we do the right thing? The doctor assured us that she might improve, and if not, he would re-evaluate the risk against the possible reward.

We also followed the doctor's advice to encourage Mom to use her brain more with crossword puzzles or TV quiz shows. Mental exercise will help but requires patience. Don't expect miracles. Pushing too hard will only cause frustration and discord. You won't be able to stop the decline, but you may be able to slow it enough to get in a few more heart-to-heart discussions. The time together is precious, as you realize it is diminishing.

Communicating During Your Parent's Decline

As time goes on, you'll notice that your parent may be more removed from reality and stuck in their own world. Trying to bring them back may feel like a losing battle. You'll eventually realize (like I had to) that it's easier to go along with them. Don't argue, get mad, or try to explain logic if they tell you that someone's been sneaking into their apartment and leaving uneaten sandwiches. Go along with it as much as you can. You're not going to be able to change their reality. You'll only make them and yourself more frustrated and depressed.

Tips for Communication

Conversing with the dementia-affected requires developing new skills. Redirecting the conversation is a valuable skill to learn. Instead of asking a question they have to think about to reply, redirect. You'll need to start with a positive statement that only requires an easy response, like some politicians do. By doing this, you'll take control of the conversation. For instance:

- Instead of asking, "How do you like your new room?"
  Ask, "Do you like your new room?"

- Replace "What would you like to do today?"
  with "Let's go for a drive!"

- Instead of "How are they treating you there?"
  Ask, "Are they treating you well?"

By redirecting you're offering your parent an easier choice to latch on to. At first, it might feel awkward, especially if your parent was once the one always challenging you mentally (as my mom was to me), but after a while, you'll get proficient at it. If your conversation lags and you're both staring at each other, take the helm and start redirecting. Even make a game of it if that helps. For pointers, watch how the staff at your parent's facility talk to your parent. They're usually experts at re-directing and pretty good teachers, also.

Here are a few more ideas:

1. **Help them with attention.** Move to a quiet spot away from competing noises to help them concentrate.

2. **Always begin your conversation with eye contact.** Identify yourself and call your parent by name.

3. **Speak slowly in a low-pitched voice and maintain an open, calm, friendly manner.** This will calm them down.

4. **Avoid sentences phrased in the negative.** Instead of saying, "Don't go outside," say, "Please stay inside." This provides a positive connotation.

5. **Avoid open-ended questions that require them to foresee the outcome.** Ask questions with a "yes" or "no" answer, or provide a choice between two items.

6. **If your question wasn't understood, rephrase it slowly with a smile and a little love.** Lower the frustration level with love.

7. **Give plenty of time for your question to be answered.** Processing questions will occur more slowly now.

8. **Never interrupt them when they're talking.** They're likely to lose their train of thought.

9. **Don't argue or contradict your parent.** Go along with them, no matter how silly it may seem. It's real to them so let it be.

10. **Don't try to get your parent to remember things they've forgotten.** Instead, encourage them to talk about familiar places, interests, and past experiences they can remember. You might learn a few facts that you can use in future conversations.

11. **Show your parent that you love them.** A smile and a hug can go a long way in communicating.

12. **If you're stumped about what to talk about, take them for a walk or a drive.** You can concentrate on the sites and live in the moment,

which will be good for both of you. The important thing is that you're there for them and that you show them you love them.

As time marches on, your parent with dementia will probably be moving on to the next level of care, where they'll need someone to help them bathe, brush their teeth, and coax them to the table at mealtime. They'll need someone to monitor their bowel functions to ensure they're regular. At this stage, they won't be as talkative as they used to be. They might have trouble forming the words that once came easily. Sometimes they may make up stories as they hear or see things that aren't there for you to see. They may not recognize your children. Try and accept this reality and help your children accept it as well. Your parent may not be there mentally, but they'll usually be happy to accept your hugs and love.

There are some simple things you can do to remove anxiety. If your parent keeps asking what time dinner will be served, make a sign that says "Dinner Served at 5:00 PM" and post it somewhere prominent—like next to the digital clock. That will help remove the concern about one more thing your parent has to remember. Repetitive actions like pulling at clothing or shuffling their feet may be signs that mean something—like their need to go to the bathroom, but they can't convey it with words. If you have pets or small children, interpreting these behaviors will come more easily to you (and benefit your mom or dad).

Wandering

No one knows what causes wandering in dementia patients or the restlessness that precedes it. Perhaps wanderers are bored and searching for a new adventure. But roaming can be dangerous if the traveler can't figure out how to make it back home. Most residential care facilities have a device that will emit a piercing alarm if the door is opened by someone other than a caregiver. To be safe, make sure that your parent wears identification at all times, just in case they decide to sneak out (like you may have in high school). Try and make sure that your parent gets enough exercise so that they're less likely to get physically restless and want to wander.

Incontinence

This often starts when your parent can't remember where the bathroom is. Make sure the bathroom door is clearly marked. They may stop noticing the urge to pee. Adult diapers have become the answer.

Sundowning

Sundowning is a symptom of dementia that involves increased energy or behaviors occurring in the late afternoon and sometimes extending into the night. It can be displayed as confusion, anxiety, or aggression. They may feel the urgent need to go somewhere or do something without knowing why. You may notice evidence that your parent was up the night before when you visit them the next day. Sundowning can also lead to pacing or wandering. While no one knows what causes it, some actions have proven to reduce the symptoms, like getting plenty of sun exposure to keep their natural body clock and hormone levels in place. You can also try playing gentle music before bedtime, keeping a nightlight on, and giving them low-dose melatonin.

Angry or Agitated Behavior

Angry or agitated behavior is a symptom that can cause a lot of trouble for all. Act quickly if you notice it, as aggressive behavior can make it difficult for your parent to fit in at a care facility. However, before resorting to heavy-duty drugs, you might be able to make some change to the environment and activities to help alleviate their aggressiveness. For starters, you can eliminate extra stimulation such as clutter in their room and keep familiar items and photos at hand. We kept a hand-knitted Afghan bedspread as a familiar item for Mom. This acted like a totem of her past and seemed to evoke pleasant memories. If your parent appears agitated, try a gentle touch, soothing music, or take them for a walk. Acknowledge your parent's anger may be over the loss of control in their life. Let them know you understand their frustration. Then, redirect by distracting them with an activity—like listening to soft music they once enjoyed. Help them forget about what is troubling them as they may no longer have the skills to confront their troubles.

Try essential oils like chamomile, lavender, or frankincense. They can be calming. Test which scents your parent responds to. I asked the caregivers to use lavender oil in a diffuser for Mom. It was her favorite scent, and she responded well to it.

Massage may also work. It can relax tense muscles and increase feel-good hormones. My mom wasn't comfortable with people touching her but wasn't against a warm footbath with lavender oil. Sometimes a hug or just holding hands can be physically calming and emotionally reassuring for your parent and break the cycle of anxiety.

Terminal or End-Stage Dementia

This last stage of dementia lasts from one to three years. During this time, your parent may need help dressing, bathing, and feeding. They may not recognize you or even themselves in the mirror. Their muscles may jerk and twitch uncontrollably. They can pull at invisible strings or moan or make grunting noises. They may not be able to walk or stand. At this point, their bowels and bladder movements are beyond their command.

When this happens, you'll probably feel what I felt—a loss that's difficult to describe. What makes it so terrible is that the parent you once knew may suddenly return, completely lucid, as if they've just been away from their body for a while. Grasp this precious moment as an opportunity to say what's important, as it may be your last opportunity. When I thought my mom was completely gone, she looked up and struggled to speak. I leaned close and took her hand. "I don't want to go back to the hospital. Ever!" she sputtered quietly. After her last hospital trip for a blocked colon, I didn't blame her for not wanting to return. I suddenly realized what she was trying to say to me. She was done fighting.

Dementia may be the most challenging road to follow with your parent. When the end stages of dementia come, you'll face sadness and a sense of relief. Sadness, as you realize that it will soon be time to say goodbye. You may also experience a sense of relief that your parent is going to a better place.

By this time, most of their words will come out garbled or so soft that you can hardly understand them. Listen closely because throat muscles are also affected by dementia. These may be their last words. They may have something important to say.

The first concrete sign of the end stage of dementia is when your parent completely loses their appetite. One morning they may wake up and just start refusing to eat or drink. The caretakers will busily try and spoon food in, but your parent won't cooperate. At this point, you'll know the end is coming. It's almost like they've decided that it's time, and they just don't want to eat anymore. Or maybe they're just not receiving the signal that their stomach wants the food. The brain may have started the "shut-down" process on its own.

As they slide deeper into dementia, some patients forget to swallow and inhale food or drink. It isn't long before their lungs fill up and develop pneumonia. They may also lose the ability to stand and walk around. Once they can't walk, talk or eat and can't understand what's on television, they may feel there isn't any reason to hang around. You can be glad you had your advanced directives signed.

The effects of end-stage dementia are difficult to witness. Seeing the once wise person that raised me so diminished was almost unbearable. I couldn't blame Mom for not wanting to live this way. The possibility of spontaneous recovery at this point was pretty remote.

What was surprising was finding that I had only a few tears left to shed. I'd said my goodbyes a while back when Mom could respond in some way. That didn't make it any easier, but when she did pass, I had a short mourning period. I'd run dry of tears. I'd been grieving for a long time. Now I just hoped she was in a better place.

It took me a while before I found that better place for myself. Most of my life had been about selfishly taking care of my own problems. Now I'd cared for the person who took care of me when I was small and vulnerable. I felt as though I'd accomplished something soul-stirring. Everything looked different. My career took a backseat to my family. Helping a parent through dementia can bring a perspective shift in which you'll find value—I did. What was important was making the most out of my time on this earth, finding meaning and purpose and creating some legacy.

Deep down within me (somewhere in deep-denial land),
I had a suspicion that something else was going on—
but I didn't know what.

Chapter 8

HOSPICE, DEATH, AND END-OF-LIFE CARE

H ospice is often a taboo subject. For me, the idea conjured dark rooms and suffering people waiting to die. Actually, what I found was quite the opposite. Hospices offer warm, sunny rooms where patients can spend their last days without pain or suffering, away from doctors and the cold, clinical walls of a hospital. We all have to die eventually. For many in hospices, the inevitable sinking into death can be an enjoyable and spiritual experience.

I found the doctors, nurses, social workers, and ministers involved with hospice tell it like it is—which seemed refreshing. There was no ambiguity like I'd experienced at the doctor's office, nursing home, or hospital. Here, people offered me the straight facts. I grew to appreciate this. At first, I was full of denial. You may be too. The hospice stage may take you by surprise.

I was at work trying to make a deadline when Mom's doctor called out of the blue. Apparently, she hadn't been drinking enough water.

"I need your permission to hydrate her," the doctor's voice implored.

"Of course, please give her a glass of water. Why would you need to ask?"

"Well, it's not just a glass of water. I have to inject a saline solution in your mother's arm," I heard his voice hesitate. "Sometimes families have their own rules about this," he replied cryptically.

What the hell was going on? Did he expect me to let Mom die from lack of water?

"Isn't she drinking on her own?"

"No," the doctor answered. "You might want to consider hospice."

That was the first time I heard the word "hospice" mentioned in Mom's care. That afternoon I visited Mom's board and care home. The director informed me that Mom had been eating less. She was even clenching her teeth when the attendants attempted to spoon in food or offer her water.

Ever the skeptic, my sister and I returned that night at mealtime to try our hands at encouraging Mom to eat more. We might have kiddingly suggested that she'd have to return to the hospital if she didn't eat up. That weekend, when I wheeled Mom under the trees in the board and care home garden, we had a little time to ourselves. She looked up, and in a halting whisper, which I could barely hear, she said, "I don't want to go to the hospital ever again."

When I looked into her eyes, I realized what she was really saying. Mom made her choice and was giving me an order, mother to son. At that moment, I faced the truth. I signed her up for hospice that day.

Hospice: Dying with Dignity

Hospice offers a way to die with dignity. It provides assistance to keep the person comfortable while letting the natural process take place.

In a hospice, a person with a life-limiting illness is switched to palliative care and placed in comfortable surroundings, preferably a quiet home. Palliative care means only medication for the person's comfort, such as mitigating pain, nausea, vomiting, anxiety, or depression, will be given. Hospice workers are there for everything from foot massages to morphine drips. Volunteers even come from the community and read to your parent or provide additional companionship and support to ensure no one leaves your parent alone. It's the royal "red carpet" treatment on your way out of this life.

Most hospice homes/facilities have core services provided by paid experts—a registered nurse, social worker, chaplain, and home health aide. In addition to the core group, caregivers may be added along with community volunteers. Some hospices even offer extra services such as home cleaning, cooking, and even support groups for the family.

Who Pays for Hospice Care?

At the time of this writing, hospice is paid for by Medicare and given in prescribed benefit periods. One can get hospice care for two 90-day periods followed by an unlimited number of 60-day periods. Eligibility generally relies on your doctor's opinion. If the doc feels that your parent's life expectancy is six months or less, no one is made to pay if your parent lives longer. A hospice patient can be re-certified for as long as they continue to be medically eligible. For those not eligible for Medicare, charity care is often available. Occasionally with hospice care, a patient's condition stabilizes or improves sufficiently and no longer meets medical eligibility requirements. This happened to my aunt. She was "discharged" from the hospice program and went home to live comfortably for another 15 years before she re-enrolled.

How Do You Find a Good Hospice?

A hospice recommendation comes from your parent's doctor, who determines when the time is right. They'll write an order for your parent to obtain the service. You can find a hospice near you by going to the Medicare website (www.medicare.gov) and typing in your zip code. If your parent's doctor doesn't recommend one, the facility they're staying at might default to the one they prefer. The hospital caring for your parent may employ a discharge planner who can recommend a few places. Perhaps you have a relative or trusted friend who will share their hospice experience and recommend a provider. Once you know which hospice provider to consider, you can set up informational appointments.

You should expect any potential hospice provider to send a representative to meet with you or your parent and discuss the services provided and answer questions. There should be no charge for this visit and no obligation to choose that provider. Prepare any questions beforehand. Below are some ideas about what to ask.

 ## Sample Questions for Potential Hospice Providers

How long will it take to develop a plan of care?

How fast will my parent's pain and/or symptoms be managed?

How long will it take to reach someone from the hospice after regular business hours?

What happens when my parent's pain cannot be adequately managed at home?

How often will a hospice team member visit?

Are there any services, drugs, or apparatus that the hospice *doesn't* provide?

Are all members of the hospice team certified for palliative care?

Can hospice provide respite care, so family caregivers get a break?

How does that hospice measure its own quality of care?

Does the hospice share my spiritual philosophy?

What kind of family bereavement support is offered?

Are there bereavement follow-ups?

How often will the hospice nurse visit my parent?

Are support groups offered for the family?

Once you decide on a hospice, they'll usually send an admittance nurse around to evaluate you and your parent. The nurse will check your parent's vital signs and ask you questions about the amount of food and water your parent is intaking and the frequency of urination. These are basic questions of input and output. With the doctor's orders, the admittance nurse then determines if your parent has truly begun the shutdown process and if it's appropriate to admit them to hospice. The nurse will also determine if the family is truly ready for the hospice process. If so, you'll sign the admittance papers.

For me, this is when the real guilt trip began. Even though I was abiding by Mom's wishes, I felt like I was aiding and abetting her death. I was giving up and admitting defeat. I didn't want to let go. Wasn't there a miracle treatment? My sister and I searched the Internet for one daily and were tormented. Neither of us could sleep.

The actual "miracle" arrived when we finally accepted reality and stopped struggling against the tide. I gathered up Mom's legal forms from Chapter 3—the Power of Attorney, Do Not Resuscitate Order, and all the legal papers regarding healthcare. Hospice needed copies of these for their files.

Then I met the hospice nurse and went over the gritty details. At this time, I learned about all the health problems the doctors never discussed with me—Mom's heart failure, a growth on her kidneys, along with her dementia. The hospice nurse was so refreshing to talk with. I wish I'd met her sooner and under better circumstances.

She went on to explain in matter-of-fact terms what would happen next. My sister and I had never experienced death up close, but we were determined to stick with Mom to the end. The hospice nurse was like our guide, switching on the lights as we entered a dark cave. She explained matter-of-factly how things would look and sound as Mom's various organs began to shut down. She let us know what to expect.

The human body enters certain stages as it prepares to shut down. While everyone may not follow the exact pattern, there are mental and physical changes that follow in sequence.

Just like every birth is different, each death is unique, but there are obvious signs that the end is near. When someone dies of congestive heart failure or a "natural death" like my mom, it rarely happens in the blissful way Hollywood portrays. Older people don't always get to say their final meaningful words, close their eyes, and quickly drift off. Dying from natural causes can take weeks or months.

Physical Changes

Aside from the sudden lack of appetite, you may notice a change in your parent's breathing pattern that can seem alarming. They may take shallow breaths and then not breathe again for 30 seconds. This scared the hell of me. I thought Mom had already passed as she suddenly stopped breathing. While I was desperately dialing the nurse, her short breaths began again. This unusual type of breathing is called Cheyne-Stokes breathing, caused by a decrease in circulation. It looks scary but is very common among those in hospice and is just another sign that the end is imminent.

Your parent's skin may suddenly feel cold to the touch, and its color may change. Sometimes even their fingernails will grow darker. This is a sign that circulation is decreasing and blood is being utilized by the vital organs.

Your parent may spend more time sleeping and may be difficult to rouse. This allows you the opportunity to sit with them, hold their hand and say your last goodbyes. You'll have time now to say what needs to be said. Let them wake naturally. Speak to them directly but softly as you usually would. Be careful what you say in the room when you think they may be sleeping. They may be listening to you with their eyes closed. Hearing is often the last thing to go in a dying person.

They may not want to eat or drink, but you can offer them tiny bits of ice, a swab to cool their mouth or place a soothing warm washcloth on their forehead. Remind them how much you love them and how many amazing things they've taught you. Add comfort by your presence. By now, they've made their decision and are at peace with it. They'll benefit from you accepting it too.

Psychological Changes

They may have repetitive movements, like pulling at invisible strings. It's a result of less oxygen to the brain causing metabolic changes. Don't try and correct them. Just try to be supportive. You could play them music, read to them, or talk in quiet, soothing tones. They may want to be alone or have less to talk about now. Some hospice patients withdraw and appear comatose. Yet, they may return and may be mentally confused over time, place, and the people around them. Don't be alarmed. This is all part of the shutting-down process. Speak clearly, softly, and matter-of-factly to them. If they appear to be in pain, explain calmly, "I'm going to put more medicine in your mouth to reduce the pain you're feeling." If some distant relative arrives to visit, explain calmly, "James is here from Martha's Vineyard to be with you."

Be kind and respectful in what you and your family members say in their presence. Don't ever discuss things you wouldn't want your parent to hear while you're in the room with them.

Your parent may wake up claiming to have spoken to relatives who have already died, or they may see places you can't see. The visions may seem completely real to them, or as some believe, they may be drifting into the hereafter and back. These experiences are part of the transition. Don't try and bring them back to your reality. Affirm their experience and give them your love. They may suddenly sit up and make an unusual request or say something meaningless. Although it may not make sense to you at the time, go along with it without judgment or analysis. You'll have plenty of time for that later. Now is the time to be understanding, kind and loving.

Giving Permission to Go

While at work, I got my call from the hospice nurse, "I think it's time to come over," she said matter-of-factly. "It's getting near the end. Wear some comfortable clothes and prepare to stay a while."

Resigned to face the facts but still anxious, I called my sister and ran home to change into some sweatpants. My anxiety was building. I arrived at the hospice, and the nurse solemnly ushered me into a parlor with two couches next to a large bedroom.

"You're welcome to spend the night here," she whispered, pointing to the couches. I had no idea what to expect. I'd never done this before.

As the sun settled, I sat down next to Mom's bed, held her hand, and talked non-stop until Sis arrived. Even though Mom appeared asleep, I thanked her for every deed she'd done for me. I realized how many times she'd helped us, and I really wished I'd thanked her before this point. Yet, I was grateful for this last opportunity.

Then Sis showed up with a cooler full of cold treats, a bucket of fried chicken, and a bottle of wine. Seeing her struggle in with such an odd assortment of goodies added a little levity to the moment. I let go of Mom's hand and headed into the parlor to eat warm chicken and enjoy a sip of wine while Sis had her private time with Mom. Our "talks" were really monologues. Mom didn't appear to be conscious, but we carried on as if she was.

Since there were only two in our family, things were simple. Sometimes in large families, your parent may only wish to be with one or two members. Large groups may make them feel uncomfortable. This may mean that they're heading inward and preparing to let go. If you're not part of the "in-crowd," it usually means that you've fulfilled your role in their life. At this point, it's time to say your goodbyes and leave gracefully. If you're part of the select few staying till the end, you'll need to provide your parent affirmation, support, and permission for them to depart. Even at this late date, your parent may have worries and unfinished business that cause them to linger in their body rather than letting their spirit detach. Your support, prayers, and affirmations can help make them feel at peace. Being there to offer support is one of the kindest ways to demonstrate your love.

Don't let your parent feel they have to hang on because you still need them. Thank them over and over for their contribution to your life, and give them permission to go. This may be a difficult task, but it's essential. Say your goodbyes out loud. This establishes closure and allows both you and your parent to let go. Share how much you'll miss them, but making closure is probably one of the most important offerings you'll give your dying parent and yourself. Take them by their hand, recount a few happy childhood memories if that feels appropriate, but most of all, tell them how much they've done for you. Forgive any long-held grudges, and tell them that you've always loved them. Then allow them to let go.

The Final Moments

At the end of life, your parent may stare into space with a fixed gaze. If they haven't blinked in over five minutes, it's a sure sign that they're drifting. Their consciousness may not be in their body but hovering in the room. You may hear strange gurgling noises coming from their chest, similar to a percolating coffee pot. This noise is from the decreased fluid intake and their inability to cough up mucus. It's sometimes referred to as a death rattle. While you can grow used to the sound if you try, you'll never forget it. Turn your parent's head slightly to help them drain any fluid. Sometimes the nurse can add medication to lessen the symptoms.

When this sound is present, the end is usually near—sometimes as close as 24 hours. Death is mysterious and picks its own timetable. Even though you're prepared to be there to be with them to the end, you may use the bathroom only to return and find that your parent has left without you.

That wasn't the case with Sis and me. After talking with Mom into the night, I finally stumbled to the couch and fell asleep. When I returned in the morning, Sis was sleeping, still in her chair, while holding Mom's hand. As the morning sun lit the room, we waited for the hospice nurse to arrive. She appeared bright and chipper and turned Mom slightly in the bed. Almost immediately, Mom's breathing began to gradually slow, and within 15 minutes, it finally stopped.

That's when I felt a presence enter the room. It surrounded us in warmth and all-encompassing love. While lounging in this glow, I heard a distinct voice calling to Mom in my head. A booming male voice of my sister's first husband, who had died some five years before. He and Mom had been close, and he'd kept up their friendship over the years before he died.

"Come on, Bessie!" he bellowed. Bathed in this beautiful feeling, I blubbered, amazed to witness this little bit of spiritual magic.

When you're present there at the moment of death, it's almost like the moment of birth. Something stirs deep within you that's hard to describe. Experiencing these events are life-changing. You're never the same afterward. I felt like there was no remorse or guilt, only amazement at the mystery of life. Mom had truly gone on to a better place, and I was so lucky to have been allowed to get a small glimpse of it.

What Comes Next

State laws may vary, but in our state, all deaths require a police investigation as a matter of procedure. The hospice nurse made the call, and the police arrived in uniform, took pictures, and asked us a few questions. They were very respectful and professional. I was still bathing in the bliss of what I'd experienced, so I barely noticed.

As soon as they left, the hospice nurse turned to us briskly. "You'll probably want to leave now, trust me. The undertakers are on the way."

Since Mom had decided to be cremated and the facility worked with a local crematorium, that part was taken care of. We just had to get out of the way. I couldn't understand why the nurse wanted us to leave so quickly. Then I saw a black van drive up the driveway, and two men with a body bag stepped out.

Sis and I drove to a coffee shop and had breakfast. We'd been through quite an experience and had a lot to talk about. I told her about my experience of hearing her ex-husband's voice and the all-encompassing love I felt. She laughed. "If anyone would have been there for Mom, it would've been him. Sometimes I felt like he liked her more than me." That made me feel better, but I couldn't help but wonder who would be there for me.

While we were having coffee, Sis and I talked about everything that needed to get done. We'd have to write an obituary, notify Mom's relatives and arrange for a service. Still, many other tasks also needed to be done. *Figure 8-1* can help you identify a few of these.

Post Death Checklist

1. Collect all of your parent's belongings from the hospice facility.

2. Using your parent's list from the death directive in Chapter 3, notify these important people first. It's never pleasurable to deliver bad news, but it may make your parent's friends feel better to know that you were there at the time of their passing.

3. Check on your parent's house if they've been living alone. Put timers on the lights to make it look lived in. Take care of any hungry pets that would be depending on them. Mow the lawn, trim the weeds and check the mail. File a change of address with the post office so that you receive their mail. Stop any subscriptions they may have; these may include auto-payments.

4. Notify their estate attorney and CPA if further action is needed to settle their estate.

5. If they haven't set up a Trust, you'll have to track down and make a detailed list of all their assets for probate. You'll need to find a good probate attorney.

6. Call the cremation or mortuary service and order at least six death certificates. You'll need them, along with your Power of Attorney, to close their banking accounts, Veteran's Administration benefits, life insurance, credit card accounts and to withdraw their pension holdings. Be sure to cancel their driver's license to prevent fraud. Check on your state's DMV website for instructions. They may require you to mail a copy of their

driver's license with a death certificate, along with a statement of your relationship to the decedent, with your signature.

7. Notify the Social Security Administration of their death by calling 800-772-1213. Call any other pension or retirement services your parent may have been receiving benefits from. Some of them offer a cash benefit for completing this.

8. Memorialize their Facebook Account by adding the words "In Memory of" on their profile. If you don't have their password or haven't been added as a legacy holder, post that they have passed. Or delete their account. Close their e-mail accounts. Cancel services such as Meals-on-Wheels, home health aides, volunteers, and all services like cable, cell phone, etc. You may have to return equipment like cable boxes.

9. Plan where their memorial service will take place and reserve it if you are going to have one.

10. Call your local newspaper and find out the requirements for an obituary. Go through your parent's scrapbook. Find out the significant events in their life and how they contributed to making life better for others. Pull out their Obituary Checklist from Chapter 3. Refine and enrich the write-up. This is a rewarding process that will help you grieve while learning about your parent's life. Include the time and place of the service in the obituary so their friends from the community can attend.

11. Go through your parent's scrapbook and find a few good photos to include with the handout you'll make to hand out at their service.

12. Keep track of bills owed: mortgages, rentals, storage spaces, and hospital expenses. These will all have to be paid from whatever assets they have.

Figure 8-1 *Post Death Checklist*

Planning a Service

If your parent hasn't left instructions for their remains, this may be up to you and your siblings to decide. Are they to be buried in a fancy coffin in the exclusive mortuary in the family plot? Mortuaries can provide all the final arrangements for the body, including refrigeration, embalming, or cremation. Refrigeration allows you more time to prepare the service. At the time of this writing, caskets typically go for $2,000–$6,000. You'll also need a carved headstone which may cost around $500–$1,500. Then there is the cost of the funeral plot itself. According to the National Funeral Directors Association, at the time of this writing, the average funeral costs around $8,000. Another online source, Funeralwise.com, cites the typical price for a traditional funeral with visitation services, a memorial service, and a burial in a cemetery at about $15,000 (depending on location).

Since 2015, cremation has grown increasingly popular—even more so than burial. According to statistics from the National Funeral Directors Association, within 20 years, nearly 80% of us will opt to have our bodies turned into ash.

My mom had opted for cremation and we'd arranged with hospice for a local crematorium to receive her body. We picked up a large plastic bag with her ashes from the facility and stored it in my garage while we figured out what to do.

For her service, we decided to rent the clubhouse of her old retirement home. I wrote up a summary and submitted it to the local paper's obituary editor. For the write-up in the printed handout at her service, we embellished her obituary notice and sprinkled images of Mom throughout her life and a few photos of her favorite oil paintings. I had some of her photos from the family scrapbook printed life-size at a local graphics shop and displayed some of her oil paintings on easels surrounding the podium for the actual service. We hired a local pastor to give a quick talk, then Sis and I took to the mic and recounted a few memories that made people laugh. Before long, her friends were working their way up the aisle to the podium recounting stories and events we'd never heard before. It was just what a service should be—a way to tell stories and honor the life of the departed while helping the living say their goodbyes.

The Service Planning Checklist (*Figure 8-2*) can help you to plan a service for your parent.

Service Planning Checklist

How many people would you expect to attend your parent's service? _____

What are a few meeting rooms, banquet rooms, or community rooms in your community that would seat that many people comfortably?

_____

Which of these facilities would be available in the timeframe you have available for the service? _____

Which minister, or public speaker, would perform the service?

_____

Basic Service Outline

Seating/Music—approximate time? _____

Name of icebreaker hymn or song _____

Introduction welcome greeting _____

Eulogy by minister/speaker _____

Icebreaker talk by family/siblings _____

Open mic by participants _____

Closing words _____

Figure 8-2 *Service Planning Checklist*

The word "Service" or "Funeral" is often replaced by "Celebration of Life," which has a more positive connotation. In reality, we are really celebrating the life of our departed loved one and saying goodbye. Consider whether it's necessary to hold this service in a church. Was your parent known that way? You could hold your service anywhere your parent was most comfortable (provided it has room to seat the people who will attend). Consider alternate venues if it feels right.

If your parent was a fisherman, you could charter a boat and have the service at sea. If they loved golf, you could hold it at an abandoned hole at the golf course. Imagine the pastor and your guests arriving in golf carts. You could have it in a local park or in a large backyard. Many parks have palladiums that you can easily rent. I've been to paddle-outs for a few of my surfing friends, where we paddled beyond the waves and sat in a circle to say our last farewells to the departed while sitting on our surfboards. The key is to make it attractive and easy to attend for the friends of your parent to attend.

Disposing of their Ashes

There are many unique places to scatter ashes. While this may occur at a different, more private ceremony than the public service, it is as important as the service celebrating their life. Here are a few places you can consider for disposing of ashes when you're ready.

- **Private Land** – Many states allow the scattering of ashes on your own private property or the private property of another person or organization, with their written permission.

- **Scattering Gardens** – Some churches, cemeteries, and memorial parks now have designated areas to scatter a loved one's ashes. You can locate one by inquiring within your local funeral home, church, or cemetery. Some countries have sections of forests where that allow the scattering of ashes.

- **Public and Federal Land** – Before scattering ashes on public or Federal land, get written permission. It's best to inquire at your local city or county office to learn about regulations. Most public parks have their rules listed online. Many national parks throughout the U.S. allow people to scatter ashes in select areas if they have a permit.

- **Ocean** – According to the Federal Clean Water Act, you can scatter ashes into the sea as long as it is at least three nautical miles from shore. Many major harbors have boating services that can provide transportation for you and your family/friends to the proper distance and back.

- **By Air** – Surprisingly, ashes are permitted to be dropped out of an airplane. Just be sure that you don't drop the urn.

Unfortunately, Mom never mentioned where she wanted her ashes spread (and we never thought to ask). It was after her service my aunt said Mom had told her she had selected Monterey Bay, CA. It was our summer vacation spot growing up as kids, also where Mom and Dad honeymooned.

Sis and I eventually made the long drive up to Monterey. We parked and walked to the rickety old pier that our family once fished off of. There was a brisk wind and the strong smell of anchovies in the air. Below the pier was a sandy stretch and some shops where we rented wetsuits and a two-person kayak.

There was a large swell running that day, and we bobbed precariously as we paddled out past the breakwater into the open sea. Our kayak felt like a tiny toothpick in the vast expanse of the ocean. We stopped when the breakwater and land appeared in the far distance. Together, we said a small prayer to Mom's spirit and emptied the bag containing her ashes alongside the yellow kayak. The dust swirled, forming the most beautiful fluorescent green glow as her ashes blended with the water. Suddenly I could feel Mom there with us, saying goodbye. The tears came rushing up, and I turned to look back at Sis. "Bye, Mom," she choked through her tears, her head down to watch the ashes recede into the depths.

Silently, we paddled back toward shore. We'd completed our mission. The moment was heartbreaking, but we'd done all we could, to the best of our ability, to help our aging parent.

APPENDIX

ABOUT THE AUTHOR

WILLIAM J. GROTE has a degree in journalism and spent over 35 years in the publishing industry, specializing in technical manuals and helping guides. As editor of an architectural magazine, his job included writing technical articles and news releases.

He was introduced into the field of aging when his once-independent 78-year-old mother began exhibiting signs of dementia. He learned "on the job" the sometimes-overwhelming complexities and emotional rollercoaster of dealing with every aspect of the process, from doctor visits, the understandable resistance of a person clinging to independence, the medical issues, finding appropriate housing – to the inevitable end. He wrote the first edition of *Helping Your Aging Parent* soon after, in 2002. Now, with the clarity of hindsight and with a newfound levity only the passage of time will allow, in this revised edition he provides a lighter, warmer, more-personal look, while retaining all the detailed facts, choices and guidance you'll find essential if you take this challenging but greatly rewarding journey.

Now retired, Mr. Grote spends his time writing, but also making wine each year with grapes from his own micro-vineyard in San Diego, and tending his garden of rare fruit trees.